THE MILKY WAY

*   *

*

THE HARVARD BOOKS ON ASTRONOMY

Edited by HARLOW SHAPLEY *and* CECILIA PAYNE-GAPOSCHKIN

ATOMS, STARS, AND NEBULAE
Leo Goldberg and Lawrence H. Aller

OUR SUN
Donald H. Menzel

EARTH, MOON, AND PLANETS
Fred L. Whipple

GALAXIES
Harlow Shapley

STARS IN THE MAKING
Cecilia Payne-Gaposchkin

BETWEEN THE PLANETS
Fletcher G. Watson

TOOLS OF THE ASTRONOMER
G. R. P. Miczaika and W. M. Sinton

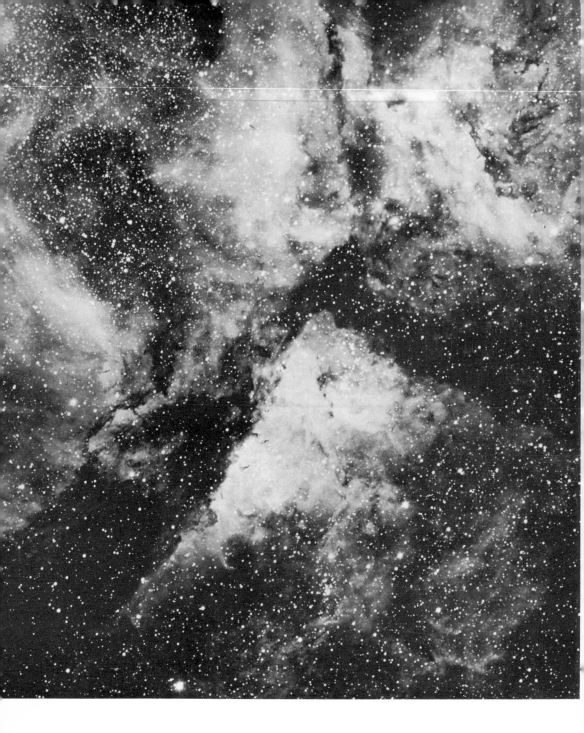

The Great Nebula near Eta Carinae. This gaseous nebula is one of the finest telescopic objects of the southern Milky Way. North is toward the bottom. (An enlargement from a section of a photograph in red light made with the Armagh-Dunsink-Harvard [ADH] telescope of the Boyden Station.)

Bart J. Bok and Priscilla F. Bok

THE MILKY WAY

*   *

THIRD EDITION

*

HARVARD UNIVERSITY PRESS

Cambridge, Massachusetts

Contents

The Milky Way

1

Presenting the Milky Way

"There is a way on high, conspicuous in the clear heavens, called the Milky Way, brilliant with its own brightness. By it the gods go to the dwelling of the great Thunderer and his royal abode. Right and left of it the halls of the illustrious gods are thronged through open doors; the humbler deities dwell further away, but here the famous and mighty inhabitants of heaven have their homes. This is the region which I might make bold to call The Palatine of the Great Sky."

Ovid, *Metamorphoses,* Book 1, lines 168–176.

In this book we invite you to join us on a brief tour along the road to the heaven of the Greeks. Modern science has provided the transportation facilities, and, without its being necessary for you to leave your comfortable chair, we should like to show you the sights. Our plan is briefly as follows. We shall start off with a quiet evening at home where we shall get out maps and photographs of the

1

territory that we are about to explore. We shall introduce you to some of the intricacies of our celestial vehicles and we shall then get under way. First we shall pay some casual visits to the sun's nearest neighbors, but soon we move on to sound the real depths of our universe. We shall visit big stars and little stars and clusters of stars within the larger system of the Milky Way. In between the stars we shall encounter clouds of cosmic gas and dust, some of them so dense that they hide from our view the sights beyond. We shall, of course, linger awhile on our visits to the palaces of the illustrious gods on the main road, but also we shall ask you to join us on side excursions to some places of the common people away from the well-traveled main highways.

In spite of our desire to show you all of the Milky Way system, we shall have to limit our celestial itinerary. Not infrequently we shall see along the road markers such as "Unexplored Territory," "Caution, Heavy Fog," or more encouraging signs, "Men At Work; Pass At Your Own Risk." For the Milky Way is by no means sufficiently well explored to render all of it open to celestial tourists. If you are so inclined, you may stop here and there along the road, get out your celestial Geiger counters, and do a little prospecting on your own. We hope that, upon your return, you will not regret having taken the time for the long trip.

So, let us look at our maps and photographs and lay out the plan for the journey ahead through the Milky Way.

*   *
*

The Milky

Way   In most of the United States and Europe the best general view of the Milky Way can be had in late summer on a moonless night an hour or so after sunset. The Northern Cross of the constellation Cygnus is then directly overhead, Arcturus is on its way down in the west, and in the northeast the W-shaped constellation of Cassiopeia is rising into view. If you are far from the glare of city lights and neon signs, you will have no difficulty in locating the shimmering band of the Milky Way, which can be traced through Cassiopeia and Cepheus to Cygnus and then down toward the horizon through the constellations Aquila, Sagittarius, and Scorpius.

The Milky Way from Cassiopeia to Cygnus has the appearance of a single silvery band of varying width, but between Cygnus and

Sagittarius we can discern two distinct bands separated by a dark space called the Great Rift. The eastern branch is by far the more conspicuous one of the two. The western branch is quite bright in Cygnus and still discernible in Aquila, but it is lost in the dark wastes of Ophiuchus.

There are some very conspicuous bright spots along the summer Milky Way. The star clouds in Cygnus are right overhead. While they put on a fine show, they lose out in comparison both with the cloud in Scutum—which Barnard called "the gem of the Milky Way"—and with several bright clouds in Sagittarius. The Milky Way is still bright in the constellation Cepheus, but even a cursory inspection will show that north of Cygnus it does not shine nearly so brightly as does the branch to the east of the Great Rift and south of Cygnus.

What lies beyond the horizon? Our summer night progresses, and Sagittarius, Aquila, and Cygnus gradually set. As Cassiopeia rises toward the meridian other parts of the Milky Way come into view and we can follow it through Perseus, Auriga, and Taurus; east of Taurus and Auriga it is lost in the summer dawn. But if we wait until early fall we can follow it southward through Gemini, Orion, Monoceros, and Canis Major. The Milky Way from Cygnus through Cassiopeia to Canis Major is, however, much less conspicuous than the branches on either side of the Great Rift. In Auriga and Taurus it narrows down to a trickling little stream that is quite insignificant in comparison with the brighter sections of the summer Milky Way.

What happens to the Milky Way south of Sagittarius and south of Canis Major? Those parts of it are invisible from the latitudes of New York or Paris and we shall have to travel southward if we wish to see them. The whole Milky Way passes in review for a year-around observer in the southern tip of Florida, but for a good view we must go down to the equator or farther south to Chile or Peru, South Africa, or Australia.

The section of the Milky Way from Sagittarius through Scorpius, Norma, Circinus, Centaurus, Crux (the Southern Cross), and Carina has great brillance. In general appearance it resembles to some extent our summer Milky Way between Cygnus and Sagittarius. The star cloud in Norma is not unlike the Scutum cloud, and the Carina cloud appears rather similar to the Cygnus cloud. We miss in this section of the Milky Way as pronounced a dark rift as is

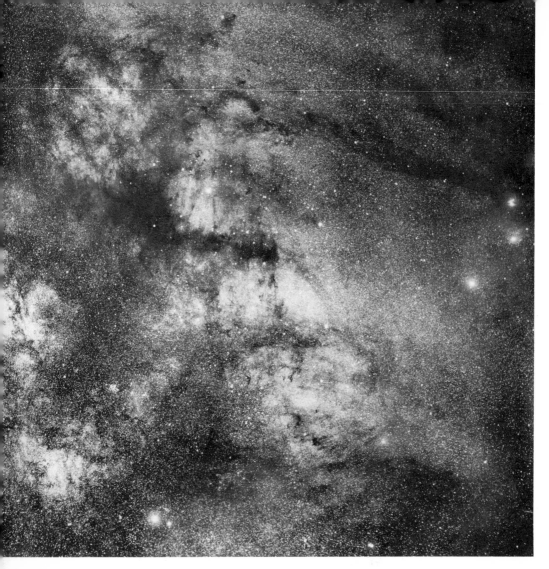

Fig. 1.   The Milky Way in Sagittarius. (From a photograph taken by Ross with a 5-inch camera at the Lowell Observatory.)

found north of Sagittarius, but the southern branch can boast of the black Coalsack, which is "blacker" than anything up north.

The remaining section of the southern Milky Way, which runs from Canis Major through Puppis and Vela to Carina, is in general not unlike the northern Milky Way in Cepheus and Cassiopeia. There are no marked irregularities, and the band remains clearly visible along its entire course. The Milky Way forms very nearly a complete circle around the sky. We often refer to the great circle (that is, a circle that cuts the sky in half) that follows the Milky Way most closely as the *galactic circle*.

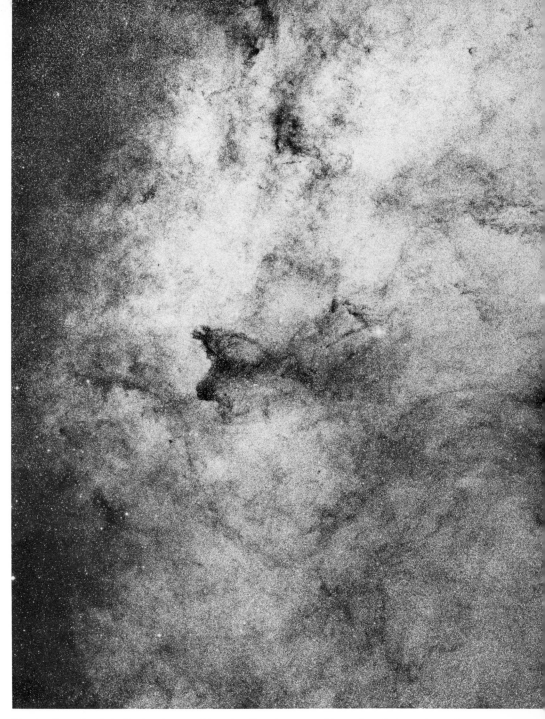

Fig. 2. Star clouds in Sagittarius, marking the direction toward one edge of the nucleus of our Milky Way system. North is at the top; west is to the left. (48-inch Palomar Schmidt photograph.)

Fig. 3.   The Great Rift near Altair. The photograph by Ross shows the two star-rich branches of the Milky Way near the bright star Altair (lower left-hand corner) bordering the dark nebulae that mark a section of the Great Rift in the Milky Way.

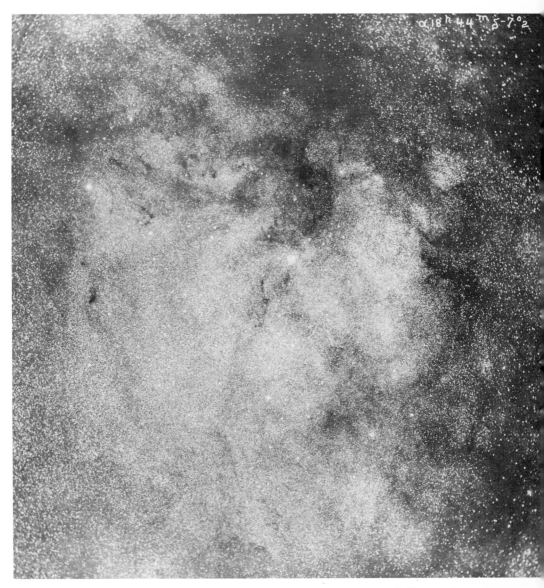

Fig. 4.   The Great Star Cloud in Scutum, Barnard's "Gem of the Milky Way." (From a photograph by Barnard made at Mount Wilson Observatory.)

Fig. 5.   A region north of Theta Ophiuchi. A network of dark nebulosity overlies this rich star field. Note the remarkable snakelike dark formation in the lower part of the photograph and the small roundish dark nebulae near it. (From a photograph by Barnard.)

Ours are the days of large and powerful telescopes and you might well ask if there is much point to a careful study of the naked-eye appearance of the Milky Way. We earnestly believe that there is much to be learned from a survey without the use of a telescope or photographic camera. Our eyes happen to be the finest pair of wide-angle binoculars that has yet been made. A telescope is useful in the study of fine details for comparatively small sections of the sky, but no instrument is capable of revealing as well as the human eye

Fig. 6. Bright and dark nebulosities near Gamma Cygni. (48-inch Palomar Schmidt photograph.)

the grand sweep of the entire Milky Way. On a good night we can directly intercompare portions of the Milky Way that are as far apart as Sagittarius and Cassiopeia. Such direct rapid intercomparisons reveal one of the most important properties of the Milky Way, namely, that the width and brightness of the band differ greatly from one section to another. The Milky Way attains its greatest width as well as its maximum brightness in Sagittarius. The half of the Milky Way from Cygnus through Sagittarius to Carina is generally very much brighter and wider than the half that runs from Cygnus through Orion to Carina.

*   *
*

Telescopic Views

A good powerful pair of binoculars, or a small visual telescope, will reveal that the Milky Way is a composite effect produced by thousands upon thousands of faint stars. As we sweep across the sky with our telescope, the total number of stars in the field of view in-

Fig. 7. Concentration of stars toward the Milky Way. The Milky Way in Cygnus, very rich in stars, and a small section of the Great Rift are shown in the lower left-hand corner. The photograph shows the manner in which the faint stars gradually thin out as we pass in the sky farther from the central band of the Milky Way. (From a photograph by Ross with a 5-inch camera.)

creases markedly as we approach the Milky Way. More than a century ago, Sir William Herschel spent several years sweeping the sky —or, as he called it, "gauging the heavens"—with his giant reflectors. His son, John, later carried out the same plan for the southern sky. Their studies gave accurate data on the rate at which the star numbers increase toward the Milky Way. They showed that the rate of increase is very much larger for the fainter than for the brighter stars. If we compare two fields, one in the Milky Way and the other in a direction at right angles to it, near one of the so-called galactic poles, with a 3-inch telescope, we get three to four times as many stars in the Milky Way field as near the pole. If we repeat the experiment with a 15-inch telescope the ratio is more nearly ten to one.

Among the celestial objects that delight the amateur astronomer with a modest telescope of his own are the clusters of stars, the galactic or open clusters as well as the globular clusters, and the beautiful nebulae. How are these prize celestial objects distributed relative to the Milky Way? Star clusters generally show preference for the Milky Way. The galactic clusters, of which the Pleiades, the Hyades, Praesepe, and the Double Cluster in Perseus are the proto-types, are nearly all found close to the band of the Milky Way; faint galactic clusters lie almost without exception within a few degrees of the Milky Way circle. The globular star clusters, such as the well-known one in Hercules, appear to prefer the regions between 5° and 20° from the Milky Way circle.

Later in this book we shall see that there are many striking differences in varieties of member stars between galactic and globular clusters. For the present, we shall say that the galactic clusters are those with somewhere between 20 and 2000 members, whereas globular clusters may have anywhere from 10,000 to possibly as many as 1,000,000 members. Most of the relatively close galactic clusters are readily resolved in a fairly small telescope, but it takes a large instrument to resolve most globular clusters. The terms open cluster and galactic cluster are synomyous. The name "open cluster" comes directly from the appearance of the cluster in the telescope; when we speak of them as "galactic clusters" we draw attention to the fact that all but a few are found quite near the galactic circle.

The behavior of the nebulae may at first seem puzzling. Some of the finest nebulae, the Carina and the Orion nebulae, for instance, are either in the band of the Milky Way or close to it; but there are others—especially those with spiral structure—that seem to avoid the Milky Way and occur in abundance at some distance from the central band. The puzzle is easily explained. There are really two completely different varieties of objects called "nebulae"—the diffuse or gaseous nebulae that are part and parcel of our Milky Way and the spiral nebulae. The latter are not nebulae at all but

Fig. 8.   The galactic cluster Kappa Crucis. The "Jewel Box" of the southern Milky Way. (60-inch Rockefeller reflector, Boyden Station.)

Fig. 9.   The globular cluster Omega Centauri. (An enlargement from a photograph in red light made with the ADH telescope of the Boyden Station.)

systems of stars in their own right, called galaxies, all of them far beyond the distances with which we shall concern ourselves in the present volume. Here we limit ourselves to the study of the Milky Way system, our Home Galaxy, so to speak.

There is one further property of the globular clusters that will certainly be noted by a thorough observer with a visual telescope. He finds many globular clusters when our northern "summer" Milky Way is around, but he does not find many during the winter when Capella is high in the sky. Our observer soon comes to the conclusion that the globular clusters in their own peculiar way favor one half of the Milky Way. They appear to be particularly fond of the region around Sagittarius, where one-third of all known globular clusters are found in an area covering scarcely 2 percent of the entire sky. Galactic clusters and diffuse nebulae are spread more evenly along the Milky Way.

*   *

*

Photographic Appearance

Purely visual inspection and measurement plays at present a very minor role in Milky Way research. Photographic techniques came into general use about the turn of our century and to these have been added the younger techniques of photoelectric and radio research. The time may not be far off when image-converter tubes and other devices related to electronic developments in the television area will supplant photography as the primary tools. But when it comes to introducing beginners to the intricacies and beauties of the Milky Way, there is no substitute for photographs made with several types of modern photographic telescopes.

Let us start with the composite map of the southern Milky Way that has been inserted at the end of the book. It was made by matching, cutting, and pasting together a series of black-and-white prints from photographic negatives made with a 1½-inch Cooke camera at Hanover, Cape Colony, South Africa. The photograph covers the half circle from the star clouds in Scutum and Sagittarius on the left, past the Coalsack and Southern Cross in the center, to Sirius and the dull homogeneity of Canis Major and Monoceros on the right.

In spite of the small scale, the composite map shows clearly some of the important features to which we have already referred. In

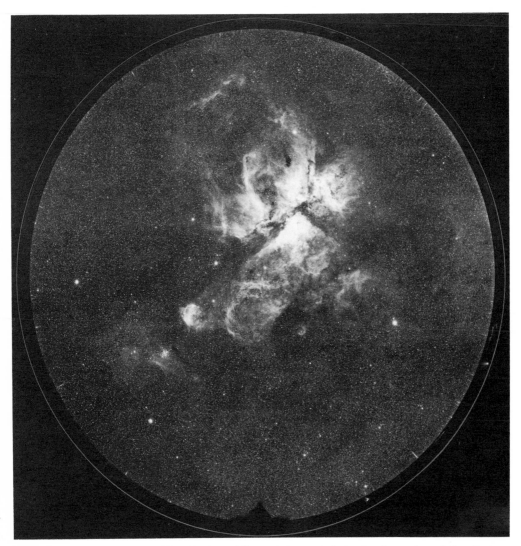

Fig. 10.   The region of Eta Carinae. The emission nebulosity for the region of Eta Carinae covers a very large area of the sky. The ADH photograph reproduced here includes an area with a total surface in the sky equal to 100 times the area subtended by the full moon. The frontispiece shows the densest section with nebulosity. (ADH telescope, Boyden Station.)

some places the resolution is not quite enough to show the individual stars, but in general we find here direct confirmation of the stellar nature of the Milky Way. The changing appearance that is noted as we proceed from left to right in the composite photograph is not caused by atmospheric difficulties or differences in exposure time, but is the result of true variations in brightness along the Milky Way. The Milky Way in Sagittarius is very much more spectacular than the Milky Way near Sirius.

The small-scale photographs used in the preparation of the composite map are fine for general survey purposes, but for more detailed studies we need both a more open scale and greater penetrating power. Here is where the wide-angle Schmidt-type telescopes and the large reflectors enter the picture. In the frontispiece and Fig. 10 we show two aspects of the famous nebula near Eta Carinae, truly the most beautiful diffuse nebula of the Milky Way, but not visible, alas, from our northern latitudes. Figure 10 shows the field of the nebula and its surroundings as photographed with the Armagh-Dunsink-Harvard telescope of the Boyden Station in South Africa. The full circle of perfect definition in the original photograph measures about 5° across, and the circle in Fig. 10 covers therefore an area equivalent to 100 times the area in the sky subtended by the full moon. To show in detail just what happens, we show as the frontispiece an enlargement of a small portion of the nebula and here we are impressed with the grand sweep of the swirling interstellar gases and the intricate dark patterns overlying them.

We turn now briefly to the other photograph at the end of the book. It is a composite map of the northern and of the parts of the southern Milky Way that may be photographed from the latitudes of the United States. The composite map was prepared by Struve and Miss Calvert at the Yerkes Observatory from photographs made by Ross with a 5-inch photographic camera of his own design. Again, the composite map shows beautifully the basic plan of our Milky Way, but we need more scale for details.

Our photographs show principally the spectacular star-rich sections directly along the band of the Milky Way. The views are less striking as we consider photographs of fields at some distance from the galactic circle. Moreover, we note, by comparing photographs made with one telescope and with identical exposure times, that the average numbers of stars per unit area of the sky are greater for fields close to the galactic circle than for fields at some distance from the galactic circle. The larger the telescope and the longer the exposure times, the more striking becomes this contrast in counted numbers of stars for fields close to and far from the galactic circle. This observation alone suggests that the visible phenomenon of the

Milky Way has great depth and that our sun is located near the central plane of a vast system of stars that is highly flattened. We return to this point in the section that follows. Before proceeding with the text, you might like to pause to look at our photographs.

*   *

*

Our Milky Way:
A Model

If this were to be a detective story we might want to present first all available evidence and then hide the solution in some uncut pages toward the end of the book. Our story is unfortunately not so simple. The evidence is so incomplete in spots that we are nowhere near the final solution of the Milky Way mystery. Under these circumstances we might as well give our "secrets" away at the start. We shall make reading easier by providing a model of the Milky Way system. The descriptive material of the preceding pages provides a basis for such a model.

Visual as well as photographic counts have shown that the faintest stars are relatively most concentrated toward the band of the Milky Way. Since, on the average, the fainter stars are the more distant ones, we have here direct proof that our Milky Way outlines a flattened system of stars. The Milky Way has great depth. Some of the stars that contribute to the Milky Way phenomenon may be only a few hundred light-years away, but others are at distances of several thousands of light-years from our sun. Since the Milky Way appears as a great band encircling the sky and cutting it into two very nearly equal parts, our sun must be located close to the central plane of the system.

Is our sun located anywhere near the center of the system? For many years astronomers believed this to be so, but if you have read carefully through the preceding pages you will find some indications that it cannot be true. One of the most striking features of the Milky Way is that the half centered upon the star clouds of Sagittarius is wider and more brilliant than the Milky Way in Orion, Taurus, and Auriga. Does this mean that the center of the system, the galactic center, lies in the direction of the Sagittarius cloud? It does.

There is much evidence to show that the galactic center lies in the direction of Sagittarius. The globular star clusters exhibit a very pronounced concentration toward the Sagittarius region.

Shapley has shown that the globular clusters are among the most distant observable galactic objects; their irregular distribution is strong evidence for the existence of a distant center in Sagittarius. The concentration toward the Sagittarius region is shared by many types of objects that can be observed at large distances from the sun, such as new stars, or novae, distant variable stars, and planetary nebulae. There is the evidence from galactic rotation, which postulates the existence of a distant center in the general direction of the Sagittarius clouds, and, finally, the indication that the strongest radio radiations come precisely from the same part of the sky.

So far we have had no indications of the approximate dimensions of our Milky Way system. The evidence on this point will be presented in due course in later chapters, but we might as well complete the description of our model now. There is fairly general agreement among astronomers that the center of our Milky Way system lies somewhere between 25,000 and 30,000 light-years from the sun, with 27,000 light-years representing the best value to date.

The model is shown diagrammatically in Fig. 11. There is no such thing as a sharply defined outer boundary of the Milky Way system. The solid line in our diagram is drawn through points where the space density of the stars will hardly exceed a few percent of the value near the sun. But in later chapters we shall meet occasionally with special stars beyond these boundaries, stars that still belong quite definitely to our Milky Way system.

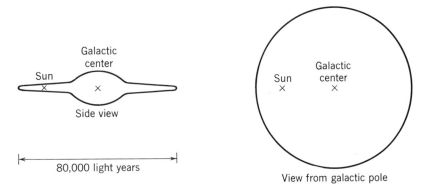

Fig. 11.   A schematic model of our galaxy. The contours are lines inside which are found the great majority of the stars of our Milky Way. The distance from our sun to the center of the galaxy is approximately 27,000 light-years.

One of the main problems of Milky Way astronomy is to obtain information regarding the arrangement of stars, gas, and dust near the central plane. Twenty-five years ago we guessed that our system is probably a spiral galaxy and this fact is now well established. We shall find that, superposed on a fairly smooth conglomerate distribution of rather unspectacular stars, there exists near our sun a system of spiral arms. The spiral arms may be traced neatly and readily through the plotting of the positions of the blue-white supergiants and of the regions of greatest density for the interstellar gas and dust.

What about the motions in the Milky Way system? The system is apparently revolving at a terrific pace around the distant center. This is hardly surprising, for the system could not possibly stay as flat as it appears to be without a rapid rotation in the general plane of symmetry. The rate of rotation is fast; our sun is whirled around at a speed of approximately 140 miles per second. That ought to be just about fast enough to suit our readers and should provide enough momentum to propel them through the basic fact-finding chapters that follow, into the realms of fancy.

*   *
*

Tools and Terminology

Each science develops its own special language, which is useful and necessary for communication but which often seems baffling to the uninitiated. To clear the atmosphere, we shall first write briefly in this section about some of the terms and concepts that all students of the Milky Way should know before they delve into the field. And after that it seems in order to write a few lines to give the newcomer at least a passing acquaintance with the principal types of instruments and techniques that represent the Milky Way astronomer's toolbox.

Milky Way and Galaxy. The physical phenomenon that we see in the sky, and which is shown photographically in the two composite maps in the back of this volume, is generally referred to either as the *Band of the Milky Way* or simply as the *Milky Way.* It stretches around the sky as very nearly a great circle and it marks the central plane of our Milky Way system, shown diagrammatically in Fig. 11. Our Milky Way system, with its 100 billion or so stars and with its content of interstellar gas and dust, is the stellar system to which our sun—just another star—belongs.

Fig. 12.   The great spiral in Andromeda. The spiral galaxy in Andromeda bears in all like-lihood considerable resemblance to our own Milky Way system. Two companion ellipsoidal galaxies are also shown in the photograph. (48-inch Palomar Schmidt photograph.)

There are millions of other systems not unlike ours in the observable universe, and we call these *galaxies.* In other words, our own Milky Way system is just one of many galaxies and we can think of it as our home galaxy; occasionally we shall refer to it affectionately as *our galaxy.* Many galaxies, including our own, show spiral structure and are spoken of as *spiral galaxies,* in contrast to more amorphorus galaxies such as the *ellipsoidal* and the *irregular galaxies.* To all but the few visual observers with very large telescopes, the spiral galaxies look quite nebulous, and visually their spiral pattern does not reveal itself. For that reason spiral galaxies are still very often called *spiral nebulae* (a name that is really out of date and wrong), and the other varieties are similarly called ellipsoidal and irregular nebulae; owners of small telescopes like to show their friends the *Andromeda nebula,* which is really a spiral galaxy. The only true nebulae are the gaseous nebulae like those in Orion and Carina or the dust nebulae like the one associated with the Pleiades cluster.

Fig. 13.   A cluster of faint galaxies. Several faint and distant galaxies in the constellation of Hydra are shown on this photograph. The uninitiated may be disturbed by the pattern of rays and circles seen about the brightest star in the photograph. The sharp lines emanating from the star are diffraction patterns produced by the various supports in the tube of the telescope. The white ring around the black circle results from reflection of the light of the star against the glass back of the photographic plate. (60-inch Rockefeller reflector, Boyden Station.)

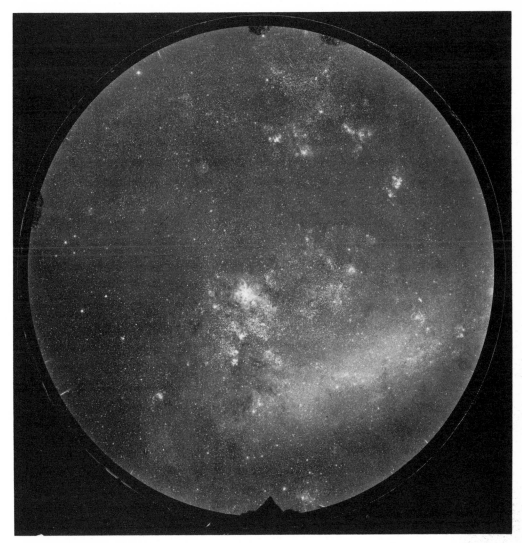

Fig. 14.   The Large Magellanic Cloud. A companion galaxy to our own Milky Way system. (ADH photograph, Boyden Station.)

The first list of clusters, nebulae, and galaxies was prepared a century and a half ago by a French astronomer named Messier, and most of the brighter objects are still principally known by their *Messier numbers*. For instance, Messier 13 is the globular cluster in Hercules, Messier 31 is the Andromeda nebula (a spiral galaxy!), and Messier 42 is the Orion nebula. Professional astronomers often have occasion to refer to extensive lists of clusters, nebulae, and

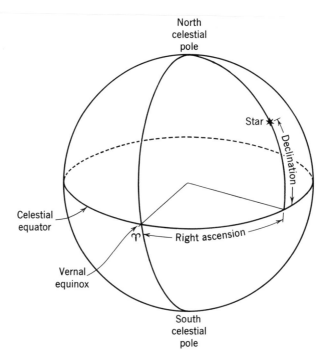

Fig. 15.   The celestial sphere. The diagram helps to visualize right ascension and declination. The approximate right ascension of the star shown is 75° (5 hours) and the declination is 40° N.

galaxies prepared by Dreyer, the *New General Catalogue* (NGC) and the *Index Catalogue* (IC); Messier 31 becomes then NGC 221. The Messier numbers suffice as a rule for our purposes.

Magellanic Clouds. Our Milky Way system is accompanied in space by two smaller systems, the *Large* and the *Small Magellanic Clouds.* Another book in the Harvard Series (Shapley's *Galaxies*) deals at length with these nearest-neighbor galaxies, which tag along with our galaxy very much in the manner in which a pair of moons may follow a planet.

Galactic Latitude and Longitude. In order to fix the positions of stars and other celestial objects in the sky, we imagine a celestial sphere of very great radius and concentric with the earth (Fig. 15). By extending the earth's axis of rotation skyward, we pierce the imaginary sphere at two points called the *north* and *south celestial poles.* The north celestial pole will be directly overhead for an observer at the

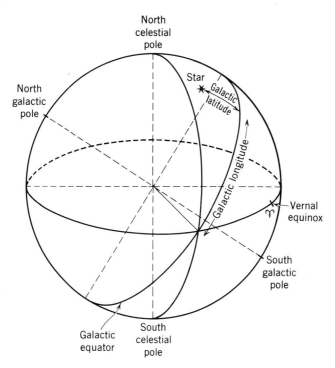

Fig. 16.   Galactic latitude and longitude. The star shown has approximately a galactic longitude $l = 70°$ and a galactic latitude $b = +20°$; its right ascension is about 20^h and its declination is approximately 70°N.

North Pole on the earth. Next, we define the great circle halfway between the two poles and call it the *celestial equator*. The *vernal equinox* is then defined as the point on the celestial equator at which the sun crosses it at the beginning of our northern spring. The position of any star or other celestial object is then given by its *right ascension* and *declination*. The declination measures how far in degrees on the celestial sphere the object is north or south of the celestial equator; the right ascension measures (along the celestial equator) how far it is east of the vernal equinox. Since the positions of the celestial poles, the equator, and the vernal equinox are subject to very slow progressive changes, the right ascension and declination of a given object will not remain precisely the same and we refer all right ascensions and declinations to a given *epoch*, say 1900, 1950, or 2000.

The equatorial system of defining positions in the sky is the basic

Fig. 17.   Mount Kanobili refractors. A 16-inch refracting telescope with two 8-inch cameras attached. (Abastumani Astrophysical Observatory, U.S.S.R.)

one, but for studies of the Milky Way we often prefer the use of a special one better adapted to our work. We noted that the band of the Milky Way follows roughly a great circle in the sky. For purposes of research we draw the best possible great circle through the band of the Milky Way as it appears to us and this circle we call the *galactic equator* (Fig. 16). The points 90° away from the galactic equator on either side of it are called the *north* and *south galactic poles*. As our basic reference point on the galactic equator we select the point in Aquila at which the standard celestial equator inter-

Fig. 18. The 16-inch Metcalf photographic doublet at the G. R. Agassiz Station of Harvard Observatory. (Photo by Cox.)

Fig. 19.   The Armagh-Dunsink-Harvard (ADH) telescope at the Boyden Station, which is of Baker-Schmidt design. (Photograph by *The Friend*, Bloemfontein, South Africa.)

sects the galactic equator. The position of any object in the sky can then be described by its *galactic latitude*, measured in degrees north or south from the galactic equator, and its *galactic longitude*, measured eastward along the galactic equator from the point of intersection defined above. On the composite maps in the back of this volume the galactic longitudes are indicated by the horizontal scale and on the map for the southern Milky Way the galactic latitudes are shown by the vertical scale.

Professional astronomers argue, often vehemently, about the precise position in the sky of the galactic equator. It is inclined roughly 62° with respect to the celestial equator.

Telescopes and Auxiliary Equipment. Telescopes of many varieties are the basic tools of the astronomer. For Milky Way research we need the best and the most powerful telescopes available. It may be helpful to remind the reader that there is a first broad distinction between *refractors* (with lenses) and *reflectors* (with paraboloidal mirrors). For Milky Way photography, multiple-lens refractors have proved useful, especially those that permit photography with excellent definition for a large area of the sky on one single photograph; these photographic refractors are often called *cameras,* even though their apertures may be 15 to 20 inches. The largest telescopes in use now are the reflectors, in which the light gathering is done by a carefully ground paraboloidal mirror covered with a thin aluminum coating. These instruments are our most powerful light collectors, but they suffer from having relatively small areas of perfect focus.

The development of the *Schmidt-type telescope* (Figs. 20 and 21) has proved a great boon to Milky Way research. This telescope consists of a primary spherical mirror, with a correcting lens placed near the center of curvature of the mirror. This combination has excellent focus over a large area of the sky, together with the great light-gathering power of the large primary mirror. Modifications, such as the *Baker-Schmidt,* are extensions of the basic principle enunciated by Schmidt at Hamburg.

A new variety of telescope that is important to Milky Way research is the *radio telescope.* In its simplest form it is the paraboloidal reflector of optical astronomy scaled up to the dimensions needed for radio studies of the Milky Way, but—as we shall note in Chapter 8—there are many useful modifications adapted to radio research of the Milky Way.

The human eye is used very little for purposes of direct observation connected with Milky Way research. We shall describe in the chapters that follow several of the most useful auxiliary tools of the Milky Way astronomer, but at this early stage a few deserve to be mentioned briefly. Success in direct Milky Way photography depends wholly on the quality (speed, graininess, color sensitivity) of the *photographic emulsions* provided by the manufacturers and on the characteristics of the special *color filter* employed for each particular project. For studies involving spectra of single stars or of star fields

Fig. 20. The 48-inch Schmidt telescope at Mount Palomar, which has completed the National Geographic–Palomar Survey.

Fig. 21.   The Curtis-Schmidt telescope of the University of Michigan.

we require auxiliary *spectrographic equipment;* to date the spectra are mostly recorded photographically, but electronic techniques are coming more and more to the fore. In the measurement of the amounts of light and the colors of faint celestial objects, the photographic plate is being replaced gradually by the *photoelectric photometer* and its modifications, and at present the photographic plate serves mostly as a useful tool for extending a piece of research from a few to many stars, once the standards have been established by photoelectric techniques.

The Milky Way astronomer pays very careful attention to his basic tools, for the research results he produces can be no better than is permitted by the limits of quality and reach set by his telescopes and auxiliary equipment.

2

The Data of Observation

Our eyes are our first tools. The sky lies open before us, for astronomy is an observational rather than an experimental science. But our eyes are weak and forgetful and therefore we build telescopes that can gather more light, cameras that can store lasting impressions, prisms and spectrographs to disperse the light into spectra, and photometers that will be more sensitive than our eyes and that will measure precisely stellar brightnesses and colors. Also our eyes are sensitive to only a small portion of the energy that is streaming down to the earth, so we must add instruments to reach other wavelengths, especially the radio telescopes to gather in the long wavelengths. Polarizing equipment also will be needed to analyze the light and detect the presence of magnetic forces.

One of the first questions that we shall want to answer is, "How many stars are there?" But even if we could answer this simple question, we would immediately want to know how many there are in each successive class of brightness. At once we have met with one of the most difficult problems of the modern astronomer—how to measure accurately the amount of light that reaches us from individual stars.

*   *

*

Stellar

Brightnesses Since the human eye was the first instrument to be used in observing stars, we should inquire into the simple rules that govern our estimates of brightness. Our appreciation of the difference in brightness of two lights is always a relative rather than an absolute matter. Two faint stars may apparently differ appreciably in brightness, but two bright stars that differ by the same absolute amount would appear almost identical, since in the latter case the difference would be a negligible factor in the total stimulus that we receive. In other words, our eyes estimate the ratios of brightness rather than absolute differences.

Hipparchus was the first to divide the naked-eye stars into six classes according to brightness. Later it was agreed that the "magnitude" classes should be so taken that a standard first-magnitude star (the average of the twenty brightest stars in the sky) should give us 100 times as much light as a star of the sixth magnitude, which is about the limit of vision for most people. Since we are interested in ratios of brightness, we define a difference of one magnitude as corresponding to a ratio equal to the fifth root of 100, which is 2.512. A difference of two magnitudes corresponds to a ratio in brightness of $2.512^2 = 6.31$, of three magnitudes to $2.512^3 = 15.85$, of four magnitudes to $2.512^4 = 39.82$, and of five magnitudes to 2.512^5, which is equal to 100.

We need perhaps to stop a moment and consider how powerful a geometric factor of this kind can be. A sixth-magnitude star emits $1/100$ the light of a first-magnitude star; an eleventh-magnitude star has $1/10,000$ the light of a first-magnitude star. With the 200-inch telescope stars of the twenty-third magnitude are recorded and measured. Such a star would have $1/2.512^{22}$ or $1/630,000,000$ of the light of a first-magnitude star. Please note that the faintest stars have the greatest magnitudes! We start counting, as of magnitude zero, stars like Vega or Capella; a star like Sirius, which is brighter than Vega, is then logically given a negative magnitude, in this case -1.6.

When we need to set up in a certain region of the sky a scale of magnitudes that is uniform and accurate over a large range in brightness, the ratio 2.512 must be maintained from one magnitude to the next, all along the way. Too many of our general and far-reaching conclusions about the universe will be vitiated if even a small but consistent error creeps into this ratio.

Our eyes are sensitive only to the small region of the total radiation spectrum that lies between the blue and the red wavelengths. Beyond the violet or short-wavelength end of the blue rays, there are the invisible ultraviolet rays; beyond the infrared or long-wavelength end of the normal red rays there are the heat rays and beyond those the microwave radio region, again not detectable with our eyes. Much of this radiation outside the visual range can readily be studied with the photographic plate and with special electrical receiving devices such as the photoelectric cell for the blue-violet, special infrared-sensitive cells and thermocouples for the infrared, and radio telescopes for the radio range. We can measure the radiation in almost any desired interval of the spectrum if we are equipped with proper filters. There are special "photovisual" emulsions, which, when combined with selected yellow color filters, reproduce photographically the color sensitivity of the eye. Magnitudes determined in this way are known as photovisual magnitudes.

*   *

*

Photoelectric Photometry

Among the photometers designed to excel the eye in sensitivity and accuracy, the *photoelectric photometer* reigns supreme at the present time. Its accuracy is unsurpassed and it is an instrument that is relatively simple to use. The light from the star strikes a very sensitive photoelectric tube, or photocell, and releases electrons, which constitute a very small current. The number of electrons released by the photosensitive surface, and hence the current, is directly proportional to the intensity of the light falling on the photocell. The electrons released by the impinging light from the star are accelerated by an electric field in the photocell; they strike a second sensitive surface where each original electron may release two or more electrons. This process is called photomultiplication and the tubes are called photomultiplier tubes. In most of the modern photocells used in astronomical work there are as many as nine successive stages of photomultiplication built into the tube and thus an amplification by a factor of the order of 1,000,000 is achieved. The current thus produced is passed through an amplifier and is then recorded by the deflection of a pen moving across a roll of paper in one of several available electrical recorders. In this way a very large amplification of the original weak current is achieved. Figure 22 shows schematically the type of record produced by a modern photoelectric photometer.

Thermally excited electric currents are present in the photomultiplier tube, even though no light is falling on the photosensitive surface. As a measure of the photocurrent produced by the star's light, we take the difference between the reading on our record when the light of the star is striking the photosensitive surface and the reading with no light falling on the cell. Measurements of the "zero" or "dark" current are made at regular intervals throughout the period of observation. The scale of brightness ratios or magnitudes is provided directly by the recording, and standard stars are observed regularly for the dual purpose of relating magnitudes to an agreed-upon zero point and of eliminating effects of changing atmospheric extinction.

Also included in the observation are so-called "sky readings." In spite of its apparent blackness, the sky background contributes an easily measurable brightness to the recorded deflections. Most of the radiation from the sky background is excluded from the meas-

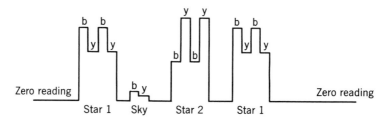

Fig. 22.   A schematic photoelectric tracing. The photoelectric photometer has usually one or more filters. In this schematic drawing the star is first observed in blue light, then in yellow light, and the observations are then repeated. After the first star is observed, a reading is taken on the sky where no star is visible, also in both colors. Then follow observations of star 2 and to close the sequence a repeat set on star 1. From the curves one would obtain the ratio of brightness of the two stars (equal to differences of magnitude) in blue and yellow light. The first star is brighter in blue light than in yellow light; the second is brighter in the yellow light.

urement by observing the star through a small diaphragm at the focal plane of the telescope, but a little bit of sky always succeeds in peering through the diaphragm along with the star. To eliminate the effects of sky background, we take two readings in succession, the first of the star together with the background radiation, the second of a neighboring spot in the sky without a star; the difference between the two deflections measures the contribution from the star alone. Along the band of the Milky Way special problems arise when we attempt to measure faint stars, since it is not easy to obtain nearby sky readings free from intruding stars. For this reason, much of the more precise work on standard magnitudes and colors by photoelectric techniques is done at high and intermediate galactic latitudes, away from the crowded band of the Milky Way. Photographic magnitude determinations are used to transfer the precise photoelectric standards to rich Milky Way fields.

One of the advantages of the photoelectric photometer is the fact that it measures the amount of light received from the star in a direct or linear fashion—twice as much energy received by the instrument gives twice the deflection on the record. Photoelectric accuracy is very high; it is possible to be sure of the brightness of any star within the observing reach of the telescope to within two or three thousandths of a magnitude. The photoelectric method has been highly developed by Stebbins and his associates at the University of Wisconsin and at the Mount Wilson Observatory. Photoelectric photometers are now standard equipment at many observatories and valuable work is being done in both the Northern and the Southern Hemispheres.

Baum of the Mount Wilson and Palomar Observatories has succeeded in measuring photoelectrically with the aid of the 200-inch Hale telescope the brightness of a twenty-third-magnitude star. To do so requires special preparations and the use of techniques of photoelectric measurement that differ somewhat from those we have described. The star is far too faint to be seen by the observer at the telescope and special techniques of setting must be employed. First a photograph of the region is taken and the difference of position between the faint star and a nearby bright star is measured on a measuring engine. The photometer is placed on a base at the telescope fitted with accurate linear scales, so that it may be shifted precisely sidewise or up and down. The brighter of the two stars is centered first on the diaphragm and then the photometer is shifted by exactly the amounts indicated by the photographic measurements. The faint star should now be centered in the diaphragm and its magnitude can be determined by the customary techniques. For such very faint stars, Baum does not measure the instantaneous electric current produced by the very weak light of the star; instead he counts the total number of light quanta, or photons, captured in the course of several hours and compares this number with the number of photons counted in the same interval for a somewhat brighter star of known magnitude.

*   *

*

Stellar

Colors   Colors of the stars are most commonly determined with the aid of colored filters placed in the light beam before the starlight strikes the photocell. One obtains a deflection with the blue filter interposed, follows this immediately with one with the yellow filter in place, and then uses the two deflections (transformed to the conventional scale of stellar magnitudes) as a measure of the star's color. The regions of the spectrum must be defined precisely and identical standard filter combinations should preferably be used at the different observatories; otherwise the derived colors may not be readily comparable. The *color index* of a star is defined as the difference photographic (blue) magnitude minus photovisual (yellow) magnitude. For the zero point the photographic and photovisual magnitudes of a blue-white star such as Sirius are set equal. For a very blue star, such as Rigel in the constellation Orion, the photographic magnitude will be smaller than the photovisual magnitude (that is, the star is brighter photographically than it is visually), and such a star will be said to have a slightly negative color index. On the other hand, for yellow and red stars the photovisual magnitude will be the smaller of the two and the color index will be positive. Betelgeuse in Orion is an example of a red star with a large positive color index. The bluest stars have negative color indices of the order of three to four tenths of a magnitude, but there are many red stars with positive color indices as high as two magnitudes, and positive color indices of three to five magnitudes occur not infrequently.

It is quite permissible to deal with the color index on a different base line from blue minus yellow, choosing, for example, a filter

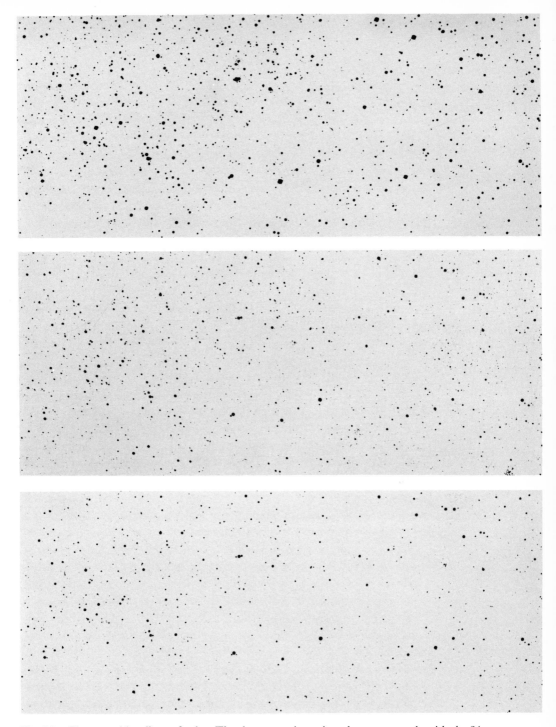

Fig. 23.   Photographic effects of color. The three negative prints shown are made with the 24-inch Burrell-Schmidt telescope of the Warner and Swasey Observatory. The print made from a blue-sensitive emulsion is on top, that from a red-sensitive emulsion in the middle, and that from an emulsion sensitive to the infrared light is at the bottom. Blue-white stars are "bright"—that is, they are shown as big dark spots—on the top print, but they appear "faint"—that is, as small dark spots—on the middle print and still fainter on the lowest print. For very red stars the order is reversed.

combination that produces magnitudes for the red rather than the yellow part of the spectrum.

Since only one star can be observed at each setting of the telescope, much observing time is needed to establish a single standard sequence of stars of known magnitude and color by photoelectric means. We need magnitudes and colors for thousands of faint stars and we must still use the older photographic methods if we want to obtain this mass of information within a reasonable number of years. The common practice today is to establish a photoelectric standard sequence near the center of a section of the sky for which magnitudes and colors are wanted en masse, photograph the region in two or more colors with a wide-angle telescope, and derive the magnitude and color of any star on the photograph by relating the size and density of its image to the size and density of the image of one of the standard stars.

Standard
Sequences of
Stellar
Magnitudes

*   *

*

The best-known of the older photographic standard sequences still figure prominently in the astronomical literature of today. The most famous of all is the North Polar Sequence, originally established— and with surprisingly high accuracy—by Pickering and Miss Leavitt of Harvard, and by Seares of the Mount Wilson Observatory. This sequence covers the full range from the second to the twentieth magnitude; the magnitudes were measured in blue (photographic) and yellow (photovisual) light. The sequence has the advantage of being located near the north celestial pole, a part of the sky that is at all times accessible to Northern Hemisphere observers. Its principal disadvantage is that it is rather low in the sky (its altitude above the horizon is equal to the latitude of the observer) at some of the largest northern observatories.

A large number of secondary photographic sequences are distributed over the sky. At several observatories in the United States, Holland, Sweden, the Soviet Union, Great Britain, and South Africa much time and effort have been spent on standard sequences in the Kapteyn Selected Areas. About fifty years ago Kapteyn of Holland selected a network of 206 centers uniformly distributed over the whole sky to provide photographic standard magnitudes. It was Kapteyn's intention that astronomers should concentrate their efforts upon obtaining complete information on the magnitudes, colors, proper motions, radial velocities, and spectral types for the stars in the Selected Areas, in the hope of deriving from these data the characteristic properties of our Milky Way system.

Competing, in a way with the Selected Areas is the network of the Harvard Standard Regions set up by Pickering. The measurement of magnitudes and colors for selected Standard Region stars at declinations $+15°$, $-15°$, and $-45°$ has in recent years been an important activity at the Royal Observatory of the Cape of Good Hope, at the Harvard Observatory, at the Kapteyn Astronomical Laboratory, and at several other observatories. The Selected Areas and the Harvard Standard Regions are so nicely distributed over the sky that preference is generally given to them in modern programs of standard photoelectric photometry.

To establish a sequence of standard magnitudes and colors by photoelectric techniques one needs numerous standard stars with well-established photoelectric magnitudes and colors spread over the sky. H. L. Johnson and W. W. Morgan of the Yerkes and McDonald Observatories and Eggen of the Lick Observatory have contributed some of the most useful lists of standard stars for the Northern Hemisphere and the lists of Stoy and Cousins of the Royal Observatory of the Cape of Good Hope are similarly useful for the Southern Hemisphere.

For the nearby stars, the color index is a direct measure of the temperature at the surface of the star; we call this the effective temperature of the star. Obviously, a blue-white star with a surface temperature of 25,000°C emits relatively much stronger blue radiation than a red star with a surface temperature of 3000°C. For the more remote stars, another factor comes into play. The light of such stars is appreciably reddened—especially for stars in the belt of the Milky Way—by cosmic dust between the stars and our sun. Frequently we may predict, on the basis of the appearance of the spectrum of the star (discussed at length later in this chapter), what the real color index must be before it had been affected by the reddening from the interstellar dust; we call this the intrinsic color index of the star. If we once know the intrinsic color index, then we can obtain from the difference between the observed and the intrinsic color indices information about the amount of reddening produced by the intervening cosmic dust. We thus derive useful data regarding the absorption of light by cosmic dust in our Milky Way system. In modern research, color-index measurements figure prominently in all studies of interstellar absorption.

The most valuable series of color indices is that of Stebbins, Huffer, and Whitford, who measured in the late 1930's color indices for 1332 blue-white stars along the band of the Milky Way. From these color indices, more than from any other source of data, we have derived our information on space reddening and interstellar absorption in our Milky Way system.

*   *

*

Distances and Parallaxes

When we see stars in the sky that differ greatly in brightness, we are naturally curious as to how much of this difference is real and how much of it is due to their varying distances from us. When light travels unobstructed through space its brightness varies inversely as the square of the distance from the source. If two stars that are in reality equally luminous appear to us to differ by five magnitudes (which means a light ratio of 100 to 1), the fainter one must be ten times as far away as the brighter one. How can we find the distances of the stars and by removing its effect find out the true range in intrinsic brilliance of the stars?

The astronomer's fundamental method of finding the distance of a star is essentially the same as that of a surveyor who wants to know the width of a river. He measures carefully as long a base line as is practicable along one bank. From both ends of this base line he sights on some tree or other landmark on the opposite shore and measures its angular direction. This gives the angle-side-angle, well known to high-school geometers, which enables them to compute any other part of the triangle. The astronomer likewise has to have a carefully measured base line and he must measure with high precision the direction angles at which he sees the star at opposite ends of his base line. We have not enough room on the earth to provide us with a base line long enough for the measurement of the very great distances to the stars. But the earth moves in a very large ellipse (almost a circle) about the sun (Fig. 24). If we can but wait 6 months after one pointing, we shall have moved, without any effort on our part, 186,000,000 miles, or twice the distance from the earth to the sun. From the two ends of this base line, the astronomer sights on his star and he will find that at least the nearest ones will have shifted their positions measurably with reference to the base line, or, more precisely stated, with reference to the background of much more distant stars.

The astronomer uses as an indicator of distance the shift in apparent position of the stars rather than the distance itself. By definition the *astronomical unit*—the mean distance from the earth to the sun (93,000,000 miles)—is taken as the base line, and the corresponding angular shift is called the *parallax* of the star. It is also the angle, as viewed from the star, that is subtended by the mean distance of the earth from the sun.

It is not difficult to compute the distance of a star from its parallax. To do so we introduce a new unit of distance, to which has been given the hybrid name "parsec." A star at the distance of 1 *parsec* will have a *par*allax of 1 *sec*ond of arc. The distance in parsecs is equal to the reciprocal of the parallax in seconds, or $d = 1/p$. The distance of 1 parsec is equal to 206,265 astronomical units, or 206,265 $\times$ 93,000,000 miles = 19,200,000,000,000 miles. Instead of the parsec we shall use mostly the more picturesque unit, the *lightyear*. The light-year is the distance that light travels in one year. At the rate of 186,000 miles per second, and with about 31,600,000 seconds in one year, the light-year is equal to 5,880,000,000,000 miles. One parsec is, therefore, equal to approximately 3.26 lightyears. The nearest star has a parallax of 0.76 second of arc or a

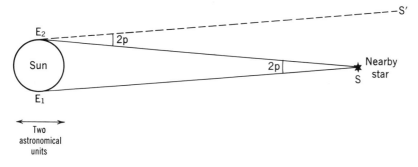

Fig. 24.   The parallax of a star. When the observer on the earth moves in half a year from position E_1 on the earth's orbit to position E_2, a distance apart equal to two astronomical units, the nearby star will have apparently shifted its position among the more distant stars, from direction E_2S' (parallel to E_1S) to E_2S. This angle $(2p)$ is equal to the angle at the star subtended by twice the astronomical unit or is then equal to twice the star's parallax.

distance of 1/0.76 parsecs = 1.32 parsecs or 4.30 light-years; light takes over 4 years to reach us from our nearest neighbor.

Finding the parallax of even one star is an exacting and time-consuming process. Photographs must be taken with a long-focus photographic telescope in order to have a large scale on the plate. These photographs should be repeated at several 6-month intervals to separate the effect of the star's own motion, which is uniform motion along a straight line on the photographic plate, from the parallax effect, which goes through its cycle every year. If the star whose parallax is being sought is much brighter than stars near it, there must be some method of cutting down its light since it is impossible to measure accurately relative positions of photographic images that are of very different sizes and densities. The modern photographic method for the measurement of stellar parallaxes was developed half a century ago by Schlesinger, with the aid of the 40-inch Yerkes refractor. Measured parallaxes are available for some few thousands out of the many billions of stars; the latest edition of the famous *Catalogue of Parallaxes* issued by the Yale Observatory lists 5822 stars with known trigonometric parallaxes. Even with the best equipment and the greatest care, the astronomer will feel doubtful about any measured angle smaller than 0.005″. This carries us out only to 200 parsecs or 650 light-years from the sun and earth. A parallax observer must often wish that he inhabited Jupiter, with an orbit whose diameter is five times that of the earth, or Pluto, which would give him a still longer base line from which to sight at distant stars! But being thwarted in the measurement of parallax for remote stars has led astronomers to devise many indirect ways to measure those distances that cannot be obtained by direct triangulation.

All parallaxes determined photographically are measured relative to the average for the background stars on the photographic plate with the parallax star near its center. A small systematic correction is generally applied to correct the relative parallax to a true one. The amount of this correction is, however, somewhat uncertain. Schilt of Columbia University has suggested that it might be well in a few cases to check with great care. He has urged that attempts be made to use as a basic reference for zero parallax one or more faint galaxies, millions of light-years away and hence certainly showing no measurable parallax displacements of their own, and thus make sure that we are really applying about the right correction from a relative to an absolute parallax value.

Before we get too far out into space let us first see what results can be found from direct parallax measurements.

*   *
*

Absolute Magnitude

If we know the distance of a star, and also how bright it appears to us, we can find its true or intrinsic brightness. We may then compare the intrinsic brightness of each star with that of our sun as the standard and have what is called the luminosity of the star. Or we may imagine all stars placed at the same distance and compute, from the observed apparent magnitude and the known actual distance, how bright the star would appear if placed at this standard distance. We call this magnitude the *absolute magnitude* of the star. Long ago international amenities led us to choose 10 parsecs as the standard distance. The formula for the computation of the absolute magnitude M is

$$M = m + 5 - 5 \log d,*$$

where m is the apparent magnitude and d is the distance in parsecs. Altair, with a measured parallax of 0.2″, has an apparent magnitude $m = 0.9$. Since its distance is $1/0.2'' = 5$ parsecs, its absolute magnitude is

$$M = 0.9 + 5 - 5(0.70) = 2.4.$$

When we hypothetically arrange all the stars at the standard distance of 10 parsecs we find that they show as wide a range in absolute magnitude as they do in apparent magnitude. The values range all the way from $+18$ to -7. We can set the sun in imagination off at this standard distance and we find that its absolute magnitude lies near the middle of the range at $+4.7$; it would appear as an inconspicuous star of very nearly the fifth magnitude if it were placed at the standard distance of 10 parsecs. If we com-

---

* To derive this equation will be easy for those who are used to logarithms and remember how we defined magnitudes. Let l be the apparent brightness of the star and L its absolute brightness. Then

$$\frac{l}{L} = \frac{(\text{standard distance})^2}{(\text{actual distance})^2} = \frac{10^2}{d^2} = 2.512^{M-m}.$$

Taking logarithms, or

$$0.4(M-m) = 2 - 2 \log d$$
$$M = m + 5 - 5 \log d.$$

Fig. 25.   Mounting an objective prism. Dr. Freeman D. Miller, mounting the 6° objective prism (showing his reflection) on the corrector plate of the Curtis-Schmidt telescope.

pare any other star with the sun as the standard—the standard candlepower, as it were—we obtain what is called the *relative luminosity* of the star. Some of the brightest stars are twelve magnitudes brighter intrinsically than our sun; they are pouring forth $2.512^{12} = 63,000$ times as much energy as does our sun. On the other hand, the faintest known star in absolute magnitude is more than twelve magnitudes fainter than our sun; in other words, it is emitting less than $1/63,000$ of the radiation emitted by the sun. The ratio in intrinsic brightness between the brightest and the faintest is therefore at least of the order of 4 billion! This range is all the more remarkable since the corresponding ratio of masses is less than 10,000. Where there are such tremendous differences from one star to another it is unsafe to guess whether a particular star is faint because of its low luminosity or because it is very far away. On the average, the fainter ones will be more distant, but we cannot say anything about the distance of any one particular star unless we know something more than its apparent magnitude.

*   *
*

Spectral Classification

Spectroscopic tools are very essential to the astronomer. All large telescopes are fitted with spectrographs of various designs; and large prisms that can be placed in front of the objectives of photographic telescopes are standard equipment at many observatories (Fig. 25). Figure 26 shows the kind of photograph that is obtained when one of these objective prisms is attached. By a slight trailing of the star's image in a direction at right angles to the dispersion, the stellar spectra, with few exceptions, are made to appear as little bands, crossed by dark lines, the so-called absorption lines. Even the most cursory inspection shows that not all spectra are alike. The Balmer lines of hydrogen are strong in some spectra, weak in others, and are absent entirely in the spectra of still other stars. The lines of iron and other metals are sometimes present, and in some spectra molecular bands are the outstanding feature. These differences were a challenge to the astronomers of the late nineteenth century, when the various spectral characteristics were beginning to be studied. It was soon clear that the stars could be subdivided into a fairly small number of spectral classes, which merged gradually one into the next.

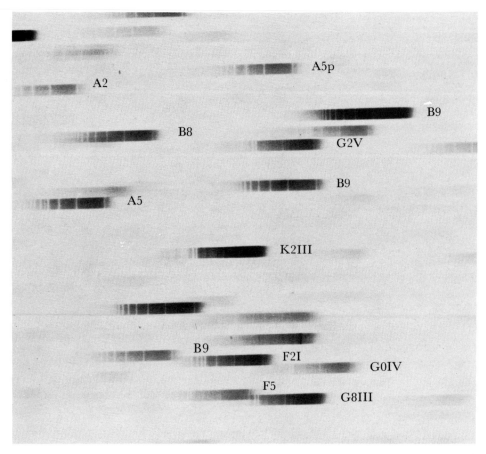

Fig. 26. A negative print of a section of an objective-prism spectrum plate made with the 4° prism of the Burrell telescope of the Warner and Swasey Observatory, with some typical classifications by Nassau marked on the print. The plate covers the normal photographic (blue) region of the spectrum.

The classification that has been widely used for a long time was worked out at the Harvard Observatory under Pickering by Miss Cannon, Miss Maury, and Mrs. Fleming. The *Henry Draper Catalogue* is the work of Miss Cannon; it contains the spectral classifications of 225,320 stars, of both the northern and the southern sky, and includes practically all the stars to a limit between the eighth and ninth magnitude. The *Henry Draper Extension*, which was completed after Miss Cannon's death by Mrs. Mayall, continues the classification to the eleventh magnitude for special regions of the sky. The spectral classes were first lettered in alphabetical order, but by a "survival-of-the-fittest" development the sequence of classes

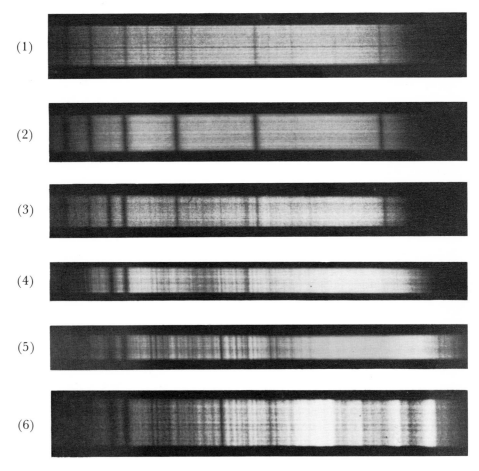

Fig. 27.   A series of characteristic stellar spectra, to show spectral classes, prepared by Freeman D. Miller of the University of Michigan from plates made with the Curtis-Schmidt telescope (see Fig. 25). Miller lists the following classifications (from top to bottom) made by W. W. Morgan: (1) Epsilon Persei, B0.5, V; (2) Delta Cygni, A0, III; (3) 70 Tauri, F8, III; (4) Gamma Tauri, G9, III; (5) Gamma Draconis, K5, III; (6) Eta Geminorum, M3, III.

has narrowed down to O, B, A, F, G, K, M. A few odd stars of classes W, R, N, and S, and some individuals craving for notoriety that are labeled "pec" for peculiar, supplement the main series. The O to M sequence is also, very strikingly, a line-up in color. The B stars, such as Rigel and other stars in Orion, are blue; the A stars, like Sirius and Deneb, are white; Procyon and Capella are of the F and G types and appear yellow; finally, the orange and red K and M stars have Arcturus, Aldebaran, Antares, and Betelgeuse as shining examples. Temperature, or rather degree of ionization, is the determining factor that decides where a star shall be placed in the spectrum line-up of the Henry Draper Classification. Pressure or density in the star's atmosphere determines its luminosity class among the stars of any one spectral type. The chemical composition is believed to be nearly the same for almost all the stars, but more detailed studies are bringing to light small but significant differences in chemical composition which hint at possible differences of origin.

The O stars are the hottest, some with surface temperatures as high as 100,000°C. Their spectra can easily be recognized by certain characteristic lines emitted by ionized atoms (atoms that have lost one or more of their outer electrons) and by the far-ultraviolet extension of the spectra. Similar in spectra and temperature to the O stars but with bright lines—emission lines—in their spectra are the group called W stars. The emission lines are believed to be produced in extended and expanding outer shells. The B stars, blue in

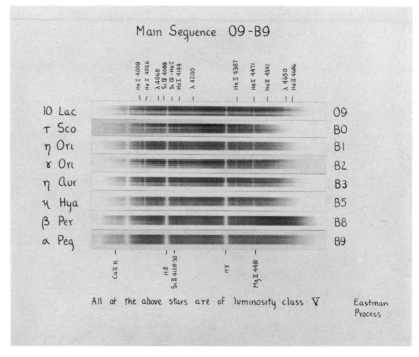

Fig. 28.   Spectra of stars of the main sequence, O9 to B9. Reproduced from the Morgan, Keenan, Kellman *Atlas of Stellar Spectra,* Yerkes Observatory, University of Chicago.

color and with surface temperatures of the order of 21,000°C, show absorption lines of helium and hydrogen. Some B stars also show emission lines. Helium fades out and hydrogen strengthens as we approach class A along the spectrum series. Lines of calcium and other metals, such as iron and magnesium, gradually increase in strength through classes F and G. Our sun is a typical G star. In class K the calcium lines become very strong, and bands due to molecular compounds come into view. Class M stars are red, with temperatures of less than 3000°C; their spectra show absorption bands of titanium oxide. The symbols R, N, and S refer to a series of cool stars (parallel to the K–M series) in whose spectra other molecular compounds are present.

There is still much difference between a "cool" B star and a "hot" B star and the system of classification distinguishes several subclasses. The hottest B star is called B0, one with a lower temperature B5, and the coolest B star is classified B9. The A0 stars follow directly upon the B9 stars. There is a wide range in absolute magnitude for stars of most spectral types. Capella, for example, has a spectrum very much like that of the sun, but its absolute magnitude is −0.4, which means that Capella is five magnitudes (or 100 times) brighter than our sun. The temperatures of the two bodies are nearly the same, but their other physical conditions are quite different. A *giant* star such as Capella has a much more extensive atmosphere, of much lower density, than a dwarf star like our sun. These differences of density and pressure cause some spectral lines to be stronger in the giants and others to be enhanced in the dwarfs.

Adams and Kohlschütter at the Mount Wilson Observatory in 1914 were the first to study the spectra of known giants and dwarfs of the same spectral class. Once the luminosity effects were noted it was possible to assign all stars of that same spectral class to either the giant or the dwarf branch, especially in the case of the stars of spectral classes F to M. Their work was preceded by that of Miss Maury, who discovered the first criterion of absolute magnitude. She found that there were some stars with unusually sharp spectral lines, which she designated by c; a star classified as cB3, for example, is a sharp-line B3 star. Hertzsprung showed that this characteristic was indicative of high intrinsic brightness.

In the Henry Draper system of classification, Miss Cannon introduced the practice of remarking on the sharp-line c stars, thereby indicating the most notable supergiants. For the small dispersion used in the Henry Draper Classification it did not seem feasible to do more. But the astronomers at Stockholm and Uppsala have since shown that even for the faintest stars, for which only low-dispersion spectra are obtainable, a giant–dwarf distinction is possible. Other observatories, such as the McCormick, Potsdam, and Hamburg-Bergedorff Observatories, have carried to fainter stars classifications based on the *Henry Draper Catalogue*. The great value of the *Catalogue* lies in its homogeneity and completeness.

The modern trend in spectral classification is to use a prism with a fairly large angle and thus produce stellar spectra in which considerable fine detail can be observed. By the use of higher dispersion we obtain greater resolving power in the spectra, but it is not possible to reach very faint spectra, and we are troubled by overlapping of spectra in dense regions of the Milky Way. The increased accuracy of classification, however, offsets for many problems the loss in penetrating power.

At the Yerkes Observatory Morgan, Keenan, and Kellman have developed a two-dimensional system of classification. Morgan studied the whole range of spectral types with the idea of finding "natural groups," the purpose being to use such groups in probing the galactic system. These natural groups are characterized by a narrow range in luminosity and by easily identified criteria in spectra of low dispersion. The *Atlas of Stellar Spectra* by Morgan, Keenan, and Kellman (known to astronomers as the MKK *Atlas*) is of great value for all future work on accurate classification. Six luminosity classes are recognized (Fig. 29): Ia, most luminous supergiants; Ib, less luminous supergiants; II, bright giants; III, normal giants; IV, subgiants; V, dwarfs.

We shall see in later chapters that the MKK *Atlas* and system of spectrum-luminosity classification and its successor the MK (Morgan-Keenan) list have proved invaluable for the study of our Milky Way system. They have formed the basis for the spectral absolute-magnitude classifications carried out by Morgan in collaboration with the Warner and Swasey Observatory. Our modern views on the spiral structure of our Milky Way system were largely obtained from studies involving extensive applications of the MK system. We are not yet by any means certain of the precise absolute magnitudes that should be assigned to each luminosity class, especially for the absolutely brightest stars, but already the success of the MK

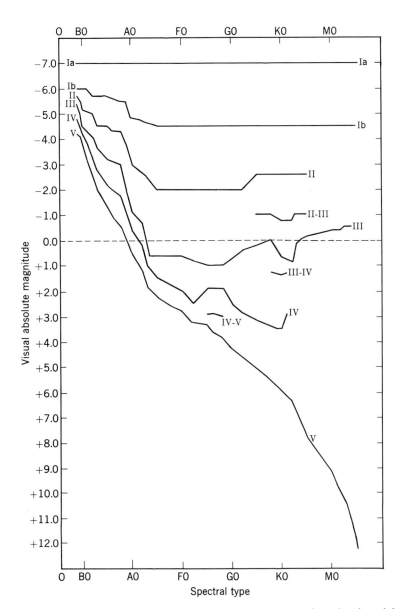

Fig. 29.   Luminosity classes. In the classification system first developed by Morgan, Keenan, and Kellman, one distinguishes both spectral type and luminosity class. The schematic diagram gives vertically the approximate visual absolute magnitudes for the stars of different spectral types and luminosity classes (indicated by Roman numerals). (From an unpublished compilation by Matthews.)

system has been so great that it supplants much of the earlier work.

In recent years astronomers have been so deeply concerned with problems of spectral classification that several independent efforts have been made to improve upon the basic Henry Draper system. Petrie and his associates at the Dominion Astrophysical Observatory have stressed the significance of the precise measurement of the total absorption intensities of the Balmer lines of hydrogen; for spectral classes O, B, and A, these total intensities appear to be a direct measure of the absolute magnitude of a star. Chalonge and his colleagues in France pay special attention in their system of spectral classification to the brightness distribution in the continuous background of the spectra, again especially for the O, B, and A stars. Astronomers favor generally a proper blending of the three basic approaches as the most effective means of distinguishing spectral class and absolute magnitude.

Another new trend in spectral classification is the study of spectra

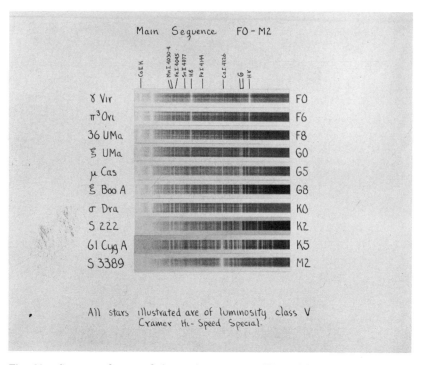

Fig. 30.   Spectra of stars of the main sequence, F0 to M2. A page from the Morgan, Keenan, Kellman *Atlas of Stellar Spectra,* Yerkes Observatory, University of Chicago.

in the infrared. Nassau and his associates at the Warner and Swasey Observatory have been the most active workers in this field. The M, N, R, and S giants and supergiants may be recognized to very faint limits from surveys with medium-sized Schmidt telescopes. The spiral structure of our Milky Way system and the composition of the central bulge of our galaxy may be studied. In the Southern Hemisphere the surveys have been carried out by Haro and Blanco at the Tonanzintla Observatory and by Henry J. and Elske van P. Smith at the Boyden Station.

*   *

*

*Proper
Motions*

In 1718, Halley compared his observations of the positions of Arcturus and Sirius with the positions as given in the catalogue of Ptolemy, and he found that these stars had moved by appreciable

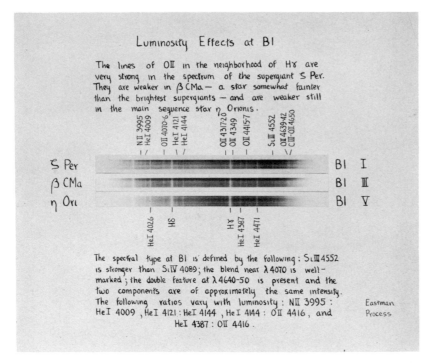

Fig. 31.   Luminosity effects at B1. Reproduced from the Morgan, Keenan, Kellman *Atlas of Stellar Spectra,* Yerkes Observatory, University of Chicago.

amounts. The so-called "fixed" stars are not stationary but are continuously shifting their positions in the sky. Figure 33 illustrates the motion of the star with the largest proper motion. This star, called Barnard's star after its discoverer, moves at the rate of 10 seconds of arc per year, a moon's diameter in less than 2 centuries. When two photographs taken a year apart are combined as in Fig. 33, the "runaway" can be spotted.

Most stars move much more slowly, so that a long interval of time is necessary for the detection of motion. Accurate observations of position in the sky are made with the meridian circle; from the altitude at which a star crosses the meridian at a given observatory we deduce its declination, and from the precise timing of the meridian passage we obtain the right ascension. The *proper motions* of a star in declination and in right ascension are obtained by dividing the total displacements in declination and in right ascension by the interval in years that has elapsed between the measurements

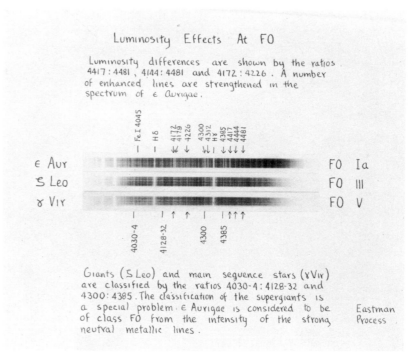

Fig. 32. Luminosity effects at F0. Reproduced from the Morgan, Keenan, Kellman *Atlas of Stellar Spectra*, Yerkes Observatory, University of Chicago.

of the two positions. Proper motions are commonly measured in seconds of arc per year. The total displacement increases proportionally with time, so that if 10 or 20 years do not suffice to show a measurable quantity, 50 or 100 years should do the trick.

It is not practicable to observe very faint stars visually. The limit for effective visual work lies at about the ninth magnitude. To measure the proper motions of the fainter stars, we turn to photography. Suppose we have two photographs of the same part of the sky taken with the same telescope some 20 or 40 years apart. If the scale of the plate is large enough, we can measure the relative positions of the stars to 0.01 second of arc. The differences between pairs of positions can be reduced to proper motions if there are enough stars on the plate with known proper motions determined by meridian-circle observations.

For all the bright stars and a great many of the faint ones the proper motions are now accurately known. For many years the catalogues prepared under the direction of Lewis and Benjamin Boss at the Dudley Observatory in Albany have figured prominently

Fig. 33.   A fast-moving star. Two photographs of Barnard's star, taken 11 months apart with the 24-inch refractor of the Sproul Observatory. In making the combined print, the second plate was shifted slightly with respect to the first. The arrow points to one pair of images for which the displacement differs from that for the others; we deduce that this star has changed its position perceptibly during the interval of 11 months.

in researches on positions and proper motions; but these catalogues are now being replaced by others of greater precision. The catalogue by H. R. Morgan of the Naval Observatory contains proper motions of 53,000 stars. Photographically determined proper motions have been obtained at the Royal Observatory of the Cape of Good Hope, the Yale and the McCormick Observatories, and at various German observatories under the auspices of the Astronomische Gesellschaft. One of the most important plans for the near future is the undertaking by the German observatories under the leadership of Heckmann of the Hamburg Observatory to determine anew the positions of the stars in the catalogues of the Astronomische Gesellschaft. Within a decade, we should possess an excellent catalogue of new positions of these stars, which, combined with the earlier positions, will provide material for very reliable proper motions.

In the preparation of reliable catalogues of proper motions one of the principal concerns of the astronomer is to find a reference system that is as nearly fixed in space as possible. All measured proper motions are relative to some reference frame, be it of faint —and presumably distant— stars, or of asteroids, the motions of which are predictable from dynamical theory. There are, however, many complicating factors; the rotation of our Milky Way system around the center in Sagittarius produces, for example, systematic motions for even the most remote stars of our system.

In recent years, attempts have been initiated to measure positions and proper motions with reference to objects entirely outside our galactic system, namely, to faint and distant galaxies. These faint objects should show no measurable proper motions. In parts of the sky where they are abundant, they can serve as a standard of rest by which we can detect and measure the motions of the stars. Shane and Wirtanen at the Lick Observatory have completed a sky survey with the aid of the 20-inch Ross telescope. Outside the belt of the Milky Way, many faint galaxies are shown on their plates and some serve as excellent fixed reference points. The present plan calls for a repetition of these photographs 25 years later, and, by a comparison of the two sets of stellar positions, good proper motions referred to a stable reference system should be obtained. A similar survey for the Southern Hemisphere will be initiated in the near future. The National Science Foundation has under consideration a plan presented by the Yale–Columbia Observatory which calls for the construction and erection of a 20-

inch astrograph at an Australian site; the Commonwealth Observatory is actively supporting this undertaking.

For a star with known distance, it is possible to translate the angular value of proper motion into a linear value in miles or kilometers per second. The velocities of the stars range from a few kilometers to 100 kilometers per second—rarely higher. The average is about 20 kilometers per second, and the majority of the stars have motions close to this value. Since all the stars are moving at comparable linear rates in space, proper motions are a fairly good criterion of distance. We have seen that most stars are too distant for direct trigonometric parallax determinations. The measurements are too costly of time and effort to be made on objects that will not give us reliable values. Proper-motion measures give us quantities that, on the average, increase as distance decreases, and so sort out the few stars within reach of our measuring rod from the vast numbers that must be gauged by other methods.

To select the faster-moving stars for subsequent direct and accurate parallax measurements, the astronomer uses a method known as "blinking." Two plates of the same region taken some years apart are so arranged that first one and then the other is viewed through the eyepiece of a blink microscope. When the alternation takes place quickly enough the main pattern of stars appears to remain the same but the stars that have a large angular motion will apparently hop on the plate. We can thus distinguish those stars that are likely to be our nearest neighbors from the general run of stars. In Chapter 3 we shall see how useful it is to select these nearest neighbors and we shall discover how crowded—or rather, just how empty—is our particular part of space.

*   *
*

Radial Velocities

When we deal with proper motions, we are concerned only with the angular displacements of the stars projected upon the celestial sphere. Proper motions tell us nothing about the velocities of the stars in the line of sight. If the stars are moving in space some must be getting closer to us, others farther away. To measure these line-of-sight or *radial velocities,* we turn again to the spectrum, which yields radial velocities measured in kilometers or miles per second.

Since light is a wave motion, it is not surprising that it has some of the characteristics of sound. We have all noticed how the pitch of an automobile horn drops suddenly as the car passes. If a star is moving toward us, the wavelength of the light it emits is shortened and the emission or absorption lines shift their positions toward the violet end of the spectrum. When the star is moving away from us, the lines are shifted toward the red. The effect is the same whether it is the observer or the star that is in motion, and the shift in wavelength is directly proportional to the speed of the star. This correlation, known as the Doppler effect, is expressed by the simple equation

$$\frac{\lambda - \lambda_0}{\lambda_0} = \frac{v}{c},$$

where λ is the observed wavelength in the spectrum of the star, λ_0 the laboratory standard wavelength, v the line-of-sight or *radial velocity* of the star, and c the velocity of light (300,000 kilometers per second).

How do we measure the shift in wavelength for a given star? Figure 34, which is a reproduction of two spectra of Castor, shows the stellar spectra with a laboratory standard spectrum photographed on either side. The displacement resulting from radial velocity can readily be seen by direct inspection of the photograph.

Since the radial velocities of stars are determined from a rotating and revolving earth, the spectrum-line shifts are affected by these motions as well as by the motion of the star itself. The effects due to the earth's motions can, of course, be computed and removed, so that radial velocities of stars as given in catalogues always have been corrected, that is, "reduced to the sun."

One complication that sometimes enters the measurement of radial velocities arises from the fact that many of the stars are found to have velocities that change in a regular cycle over a period of time. A companion star—often invisible—may be present and the two stars revolve about each other under their mutual gravitation. These *double stars* are very interesting in themselves and from them we derive information about the masses of the stars, but they have delayed considerably the determination of the radial velocities of the fainter stars. Enough spectral photographs of a double star must be taken to find out how much of the observed speed is due to the orbital motion and how much to the velocity of the system as a whole.

Much of the early exact radial-velocity work was done by Campbell, Wright, and Moore at the Lick Observatory with the 36-inch telescope and the three-prism Mills spectrograph. The Lick

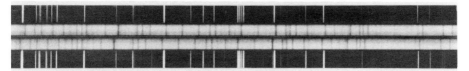

Fig. 34.   Radial-velocity effects in Castor. The bright bands in the center crossed by dark lines are two spectra of the same component of Castor taken at different times. The bright lines on either side are the comparison spectrum, photographed at the same time as the star's spectrum to serve as a standard of reference. Each component of the double star Castor is itself a spectroscopic binary. The upper one of the star's spectra shows a radial displacement due to a velocity of recession of 24 mi/sec; the lower one shows a radial velocity displacement of approach amounting to 32 mi/sec. (Lick Observatory photograph.)

Catalogue of Radial Velocities includes almost all naked-eye stars in both hemispheres. Several observatories are engaged upon the measurement of radial velocities of the fainter stars. In the planning of specific research programs, each observatory concentrates upon a certain spectral group, or on some special type of star, such as Cepheid variables. The task of representative coverage for the fainter stars of the Northern and Southern Hemispheres is a huge one. The lack of sufficient radial velocities is felt especially for the southern stars, but the Radcliffe Observatory at Pretoria is busy filling the gap and the Australian Commonwealth Observatory has joined in the effort. From time to time catalogues, which bring together all available data, are prepared; the most recent one was published by R. E. Wilson of the Mount Wilson and Palomar Observatories and gives the radial velocities for 15,107 stars.

Modern instrumental developments have speeded up the work on spectra of fainter stars. Mirrors are now covered with aluminum instead of silver, to reach farther into the ultraviolet; highly transparent optical glass of excellent quality is available for prisms; and gratings are made that concentrate most of the light in one spectrum. Cameras of the Schmidt type and very sensitive photographic emulsions all help to reach fainter stars so that we can find the speeds with which they are traveling and build up our picture of the motions of the whole system.

Thus far we have dealt only with measurements of radial velocities star by star, one at a time. Beside the spectrum of each star, we impress on our photograph a comparison spectrum, produced by a luminous source mounted near the slit on the spectrograph. This gives the necessary reference lines against which we can measure the shifts of the lines in the star's spectrum. It would help to speed up the determination of radial velocities for faint stars if we could derive from one single photograph the radial velocities of a considerable number of stars.

Numerous attempts have been made to obtain radial velocities en masse from objective-prism plates, which record many stars simultaneously. The hardest problem is to obtain some reference point against which to measure the shift due to radial velocity. One approach, originally developed by Pickering and perfected by Bok and McCuskey at Harvard Observatory, was to use a liquid absorption filter, filled with a solution of neodymium chloride and placed in front of the photographic plate. In each spectrum a molecular absorption band is produced, which closely resembles a stellar absorption line and serves as the desired reference zero for radial-velocity measurements. To date, the absorption method has not given results of quite the desired accuracy, but the basic technique is capable of further development.

Encouraging results have been obtained by Fehrenbach at the Haute Provence Observatory with a scheme according to which the objective prism is rotated through precisely 180° several times in the course of one exposure. The result is that each star has two images, one with the violet end of the spectrum to the left, the other with the violet to the right. The distance between the two images of the same spectral line in a star can be used to derive the displacement due to the star's radial velocity. The Fehrenbach technique looks very promising and should provide an abundance of useful material relating to the radial velocities of faint stars.

*   *

*

Coöperation
in Research   The tradition of coöperation in research is deeply rooted in the astronomical profession. There are many reasons why this is so. First, the number of research astronomers in the world is not large (hardly more than 1000) and there is so much work to be done that some sharing of effort is necessary to achieve common research goals. Second, we are all dealing with the same physical universe, and some consultation between workers in the same areas of research activity is necessary if we wish to avoid duplication of effort. Third, it is difficult to combine results by different observers unless

a special effort is made to have the observations on a comparable basis; for example, in magnitude and color measurements we prefer to have all observers accept common standards and use clearly specified color filters that permit reduction from one color system to another; in proper-motion work, we prefer to have all of our motions referred to a single established fundamental system of positions and motions. Fourth, the telescopic and auxiliary equipment is often so expensive that one institution or one nation (especially the smaller ones) cannot afford to build what they would like to use, and thus coöperative ownership and management become essential.

Organized coöperative research relating to the structure and motions of our Milky Way system originated in the second half of the nineteenth century. The two most famous examples were the *Astrographic Catalogue,* an attempt to photograph the entire sky in zones of declination with each participating observatory assuming responsibility for the measurement of the positions of the stars on the photographs in its assigned zone, and the Astronomische Gesellschaft *Catalogue,* primarily a German undertaking, to provide accurate meridian-circle positions for large numbers of stars.

The most far-reaching effort to effect international coöperation was that initiated by Kapteyn in 1904 at Groningen in Holland— the so-called "Plan of Selected Areas" of which we have already spoken. Kapteyn's plan captured the imagination of the astronomical world and as a result of his appeal we now possess for many stars in the Selected Areas accurate measures of positions, proper motions, radial velocities, magnitudes, spectral types, and color indices. Parallaxes are still largely lacking.

In the early 1920's the need was felt for a broad international organization embodying the whole of astronomy, and, in consequence, the International Astronomical Union was established. The I.A.U.—by which three initials the organization is known throughout the astronomical world—held its first formal meeting in 1922 in Rome; it has met since then once every three or four years, with only one longer interval between meetings—that caused by World War II. The principal continuing function of the I.A.U. is to provide through its forty or more permanent commissions a medium for international contact between workers in the same field the world over. The I.A.U. has been responsible for the initiation of many new coöperative projects and it serves as the clearing house for older programs like those mentioned above. Whenever the need arises, the I.A.U., with the support of UNESCO, initiates conferences with a limited number of specialists in attendance. An example is the Conference on Coördination of Galactic Research held at Groningen in June 1953. This Conference surveyed the whole field of Milky Way work and studied especially ways in which the Kapteyn Plan of Selected Areas could be modified to be of greatest service to the advance of Milky Way investigations. The attendance was small (30 astronomers from 11 countries), but out of this conference have come new projects that should change the face of Milky Way research.

A new form of coöperation is one by which astronomers associated with different observatories share common research facilities. The plan for a new large coöperative observatory of five or more Western European nations, to be built in South Africa, is of this type. None of the countries alone can build and maintain a major Southern Hemisphere observatory with a 120-inch reflector and a large Schmidt-type telescope, but together they may be able to do so. A different example of this same trend is the arrangement by which five Western European observatories share with Harvard Observatory responsibility for the management and operation of the Boyden Station in South Africa. The Australian Commonwealth Observatory plays host to observing stations from Yale and Columbia and from Upsala in Sweden. In the United States, some of the large southwestern observatories make their equipment available to astronomers from observatories with less powerful equipment and with less favorable conditions for astronomical observation. The National Science Foundation is taking the lead in promoting the growth of coöperative research facilities in the United States; a National Radio Observatory and a National Optical Observatory are important items on the high-priority list. These coöperative efforts hold great promise for the future development of astronomy; Milky Way research stands to profit by them as much as any branch of astronomy.

3

The Sun's Nearest Neighbors

How does the sun rate among the stars? Is it very brilliant, is it average, or somewhat dull? As students of the Milky Way we are interested in the answers to these questions not so much because we care about the sun itself as because we wish to know what variety exists among the stars and just what proportions there are of the different kinds in a sample of space—and how uniform our sample remains in different parts of the Milky Way.

*   *
*

We shall consider here two lists of stars that have been recently published by van de Kamp of Swarthmore College.

The first list (Table 1) includes all the very bright stars that we know by name, together with some bright southern ones that we

TABLE 1. THE TWENTY BRIGHTEST STARS.*

No.	Name	Visual apparent magnitude †	Spectrum	Absolute magnitude	Luminosity	Distance (light-years)
1	Sirius	−1.6^d	A0	+1.3	23	8.7
2	Canopus	−0.9	F0	−4.6:	5200:	180:
3	Alpha Centauri	0.3^t	G0	+4.7	1.0	4.29
4	Vega	0.1	A0	+0.5	48	26.5
5	Capella	0.2^t	G0	−0.5	120	45
6	Arcturus	0.2	K0	0.0	76	36
7	Rigel	0.3	B8pec	−6.2:	23,000:	650:
8	Procyon	0.5^d	F5	+2.8	5.8	11.3
9	Achenar	0.6	B5	−2.6:	800:	140:
10	Beta Centauri	0.9	B1	−3.1:	1300:	200:
11	Altair	0.9	A5	+2.4	8.3	16.5
12	Betelgeuse	(0.9) var.	M2	(−5.6:)	13,000:	650:
13	Alpha Crucis	1.4^d	B1	−2.7:	900:	220:
14	Aldebaran	1.1^d	K5	−0.5	120	68
15	Pollux	1.2	K0	+1.0	30	35
16	Spica	1.2	B2	−2.2:	600:	160:
17	Antares	1.2^d	M1	−2.4:	700:	170:
18	Fomalhaut	1.3	A3	+2.1	11	23
19	Deneb	1.3	A2pec	−4.8:	6000:	540:
20	Regulus	1.3^d	B8	−0.7	140	84

* The mark : indicates uncertainty in the values given, due to the difficulty in determining the exact value of the parallax for distant stars.
† d, double; t, triple.

are unable to see from northern latitudes. They show a wide range in color, from blue Rigel and Spica, yellow Capella, and orange Arcturus, to red Betelgeuse and Antares. For all these stars, values of the parallax and distance are available, but for the more distant ones the values are uncertain; their parallaxes are of the same size as the unavoidable errors of measurement.

Figure 35 shows how the brightest stars vary in spectral class and in absolute magnitude. All spectral classes are present, but 11 out of the 20 are the very hot B or A stars. All but one of these 20 are more luminous than the sun, with its visual absolute magnitude of 4.7. In fact, Rigel shines as brightly as 23,000 suns and four others are more than a thousand times as bright as the sun.

The star that comes closest to being a twin of our sun in spectrum

and luminosity is our nearest neighbor, Alpha Centauri. It is only
4.3 light-years away. Rigel, which is the most distant, is about 650
light-years away, a distance too great for the accurate measurement
of parallax. If we consider the volume of space that we have covered
before we caught a star such as Rigel, we see that it is some
$(650/4)^3$ or about 4,000,000 times as large as that we would have
to explore to find Alpha Centauri. We may catch a minnow in our
hands close to shore, but we must sail far if we wish to harpoon a
whale! We begin to suspect that such stars as Rigel, and to a lesser
extent the other bright B stars, must be very rare objects in space
as compared with our sun and its like.

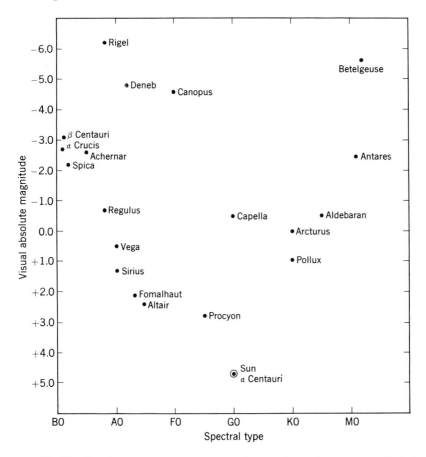

Fig. 35. The brightest stars. The diagram is based on the data of Table 1
and shows a visual absolute magnitude plotted against spectral type. (Data from
van de Kamp.)

TABLE 2. THE NEAREST STARS.

No.	Name	Visual apparent magnitude	Spectrum	Absolute magnitude	Luminosity	Distance (light-years)
1	Sun	−26.9	G0	4.7	1.0	——
2	Alpha Centauri A	0.3	G0	4.7	1.0	4.3
3	Alpha Centauri B	1.7	K5	6.1	0.28	4.3
4	Alpha Centauri C	11	M5e	15.4	.000052	4.3
5	Barnard's star	9.5	M5	13.2	.00040	6.0
6	Wolf 359	13.5	M6e	16.6	.000017	7.7
7	Luyten 726–8 A	12.5	M6e	15.6	.00004	7.9
8	Luyten 726–8 B	13.0	M6e	16.1	.00003	7.9
9	Lalande 21185	7.5	M2	10.5	.0048	8.2
10	Sirius A	−1.6	A0	1.3	23	8.7
11	Sirius B	7.1	wd	10.0	0.008	8.7
12	Ross 154	10.6	M5e	13.3	.00036	9.3
13	Ross 248	12.2	M6e	14.7	.00010	10.3
14	Epsilon Eridani	3.8	K2	6.2	.25	10.8
15	Ross 128	11.1	M5	13.5	.00030	10.9
16	61 Cygni A	5.6	K6	7.9	.052	11.1
17	61 Cygni B	6.3	M0	8.6	.028	11.1
18	Luyten 789–6	12.2	M6	14.5	.00012	11.2
19	Procyon A	0.5	F5	2.8	5.8	11.3
20	Procyon B	10.8	wd	13.1	0.00044	11.3
21	Epsilon Indi	4.7	K5	7.0	.12	11.4
22	Σ 2398 A	8.9	M4	11.1	.0028	11.6
23	Σ 2398 B	9.7	M4	11.9	.0013	11.6
24	Groombridge 34 A	8.1	M2e	10.3	.0058	11.7
25	Groombridge 34 B	10.9	M4e	13.1	.00044	11.7
26	Tau Ceti	3.6	G4	5.8	.36	11.8
27	Lacaille 9352	7.2	M2	9.4	.013	11.9
28	BD +5° 1668	10.1	M4	12.2	.0010	12.4
29	Lacaille 8760	6.6	M1	8.6	.028	12.8
30	Kapteyn's star	9.2	M0	11.2	.0025	13.0
31	Kruger 60 A	9.9	M4	11.9	.0013	13.1
32	Kruger 60 B	11.4	M5e	13.4	.00033	13.1
33	Ross 614 A	10.9	M5e	12.9	.00052	13.1
34	Ross 614 B	14.8	—	16.8	.000014	13.1
35	BD −12° 4523	10.0	M5	11.9	.0013	13.4
36	van Maanen's star	12.3	wdF	14.2	.00016	13.8
37	Wolf 424 A	12.6	M6e	14.3	.00014	14.6
38	Wolf 424 B	12.6	M6e	14.3	.00014	14.6

Table 2.   THE NEAREST STARS. (*Continued*)

No.	Name	Visual apparent magnitude	Spectrum	Absolute magnitude	Luminosity	Distance (light-years)
39	Groombridge 1618	6.8	K5	8.5	.030	14.7
40	CD −37° 15492	8.6	M3	10.3	.0058	14.9
41	CD −46° 11540	9.7	M4	11.3	.0023	15.3
42	BD +20° 2465	9.5	M4e	11.1	.0028	15.4
43	CD −44° 11909	11.2	M5	12.8	.00058	15.6
44	CD −49° 13515	9	M3	10.6	.0044	15.6
45	AOe 17415–6	9.1	M3	10.7	.0040	15.8
46	Ross 780	10.2	M5	11.8	.0014	15.8
47	Lalande 25372	8.6	M2	10.2	.0063	15.9
48	CC 658	11	wd	12.5	.0008	16.0
49	Omicron² Eridani A	4.5	K0	6.0	.30	16.3
50	Omicron² Eridani B	9.2	wdA	10.7	.0040	16.3
51	Omicron² Eridani C	11.0	M5e	12.5	.0008	16.3
52	70 Ophiuchi A	4.2	K1	5.7	.40	16.4
53	70 Ophiuchi B	5.9	K5	7.4	.083	16.4
54	Altair	0.9	A5	2.4	8.3	16.5
55	BD +43° 4305	10.2	M5e	11.7	0.0016	16.5
56	AC 79° 3888	11.0	M4	12.5	.0008	16.6

The M-type star Betelgeuse is also a very luminous star at much the same distance as Rigel. Since its surface is comparatively cool it must be very large to give off so much light. Betelgeuse and Antares are among the very few stars for which the apparent diameter can be measured, with the aid of an instrument called an interferometer; the diameter of Betelgeuse has been found to measure 4 astronomical units, that of Antares about 3. A star that is so big that Mars could follow its whole path inside the star is indeed a giant! Betelgeuse is variable in brightness and perhaps also changes in size with an irregular period.

Let us next look at the list of nearby stars given in Table 2. Included are all stars that are known to be within a distance from the sun of 5 parsecs or 16.6 light-years. We find that the four brightest stars in this list—Sirius, Altair, Procyon, and Alpha Centauri—were also in Table 1. They are conspicuous stars in our sky because they are nearby rather than because of their exceptional luminosity. The rest of the stars are much fainter, both apparently

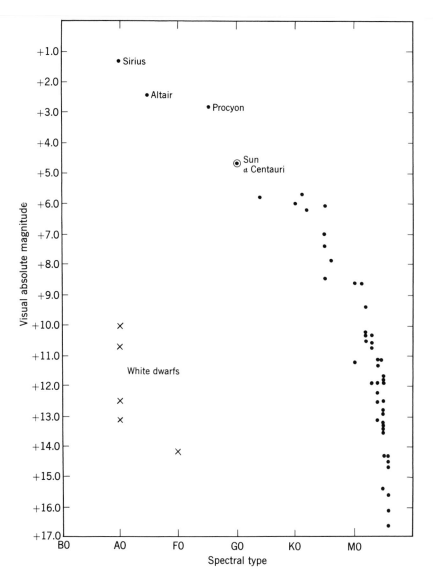

Fig. 36.   The nearest stars. Table 2 is the source of data for this diagram, in which visual absolute magnitude is plotted against spectral type. (Data from van de Kamp.)

and absolutely. Figure 36 shows how these stars vary in spectral class and absolute magnitude.

Unlike our first list, we cannot be sure that our second list is complete. A few stars have been added in the last 10 years and a certain amount of reshuffling has taken place as more accurate values of the parallaxes have been determined. No doubt there will be more additions in the future. There are many faint stars with large proper motions the parallaxes of which have not been measured, and time will undoubtedly add to the number of our faint neighbors. It is not believed, however, that the number will be increased very greatly. From the average speed of the stars near our sun the average total density of matter in our region of space can be estimated. This value, which is a little under one-tenth of a solar mass for a cube 1 parsec [= 3.26 light-years] on a side, is very close to the value of the average space density that we find in the sphere with a radius of 16 light-years, if we make reasonable assumptions as to the masses of these nearby stars and take account of the contribution from the interstellar gas and dust.

There are some very real differences between the kinds of stars on our two lists. The first list contains almost entirely what are known as giants and supergiants. They are of all spectral classes from B through M. Our second list comprises the dwarfs, or, as we prefer to call them, the "main-sequence" stars. We see in Fig. 36 the very definite tendency for the stars to fall along a diagonal line, so that they become fainter as they become redder. We find no stars of class K or M that are of the same absolute magnitude as our sun; they are either brighter or fainter. Among our nearby stars we find none of the brilliant B stars or G, K, or M giants. These show up among the naked-eye stars because of their high intrinsic luminosities, but actually they are very rare objects in space, and those that we see are well beyond our 16-light-year sphere.

The most common variety of stars in Table 2 is the faint red dwarf of class M. These stars make up almost two-thirds of the list of our neighbors and range in luminosity from 0.01 to 1/60,000 that of the sun. Van de Kamp points out that the faintest known star, only one-tenth as bright as the faintest in our list, lies outside this 16-light-year sphere; it is van Biesbroeck's star, and its distance from the sun is 19 light-years. We may reasonably expect that there will be additions to our list at the tail end of the line.

Many of the M dwarfs are known as "flare stars." While their usual luminosity is very low, they may on occasion brighten up by two magnitudes or more in a brief interval, and several have repeated this flare-up more than once. Bright lines are observed in their spectra.

We should bring out here clearly that our list of 56 nearby stars (including the sun) contains only 42 separate systems. Ten of these 42 stars are double, while two others are triple. In addition there are four with as yet unseen companions. These invisible companions have been discovered by the perturbations in proper motions of the visible star. Their masses begin to approach the range of planetary masses as we know them in our solar system; they are of the order of a few hundredths of the solar mass, whereas Jupiter has a mass 0.001 that of the sun. The companion to Ross 614A has been shown by Miss Lippincott to be a star of very low mass, one twelfth that of the sun. Luyten has pointed to a double star for which the mass of each component is even smaller, probably no greater than one twenty-fifth the mass of the sun. According to Luyten, the faintest recorded visual absolute magnitude for a star equals $+17.2$, which corresponds to an intrinsic brightness of the order of 0.00001 that of the sun.

Our list of the nearest stars contains five blue-white stars of very low intrinsic brightness, the representatives of the class of *white dwarfs*. These white dwarfs constitute a most interesting group among our neighbors, the most famous one being the companion of Sirius. Two others are companions, while two are single. When the companion of Sirius was discovered, its high temperature combined with its low luminosity suggested a most unusual object and probably a very rare one. No one had previously considered the possibility of the existence of stars with masses only slightly less than that of the sun but with radii hardly larger than that of the earth. The searches of Luyten, supplemented by subsequent studies by Luyten and Kuiper, have shown that white dwarfs may be as common objects as stars like our sun. Altogether Luyten has identified about 100 of these stars, which he calls "the easiest stars to identify and the hardest to observe." The criteria for their discovery are large proper motions and a color index comparable to that of an unreddened B or A star.

The bulk of the known white dwarfs are of the fourteenth apparent magnitude. For more than half of those discovered, spectra and parallaxes have been determined, so that they can be fitted into a spectrum–absolute magnitude array. They form a progression not quite parallel to the main sequence with luminosities from about 1/20 to 1/60,000 that of the sun. Several are found as companions to other stars, so that their masses can be determined and their sizes estimated. Most of them seem to range in size between the planet Mercury and the planet Uranus, between one-third and four times the size of the earth.

For the brightest stars we did not include the companions on the list. Five of the 20 brightest stars are double, 3 are triple, and 5 are spectroscopic binaries. Thus our list of 20 stars really contain 36 objects. Duplicity is common among the stars.

More recent tables of the 30 brightest stars and the nearest stars were published by Herbig and Worley at the Lick Observatory after our tables had gone to press. Our list of the 20 brightest stars is the same as their list but the order is slightly changed owing to the use of more recent and accurate photoelectrically determined apparent magnitudes. The spectral types and luminosity classes are given in the Morgan-Keenan system. For the most distant stars the differences show clearly the uncertainties of luminosity determinations based on trigonometric parallaxes. The case of the most extreme uncertainty is that of Rigel for which van de Kamp's luminosity is 23,000 times that of the sun and Herbig and Worley's is 50,000; this represents a difference in assigned absolute magnitude of a little under 1 magnitude. The new list of nearest stars differs little from ours. Slight changes are brought out by a presumably more accurate spectral classification and some newly determined apparent magnitudes.

*   *

*

The Hertzsprung-Russell Diagram

The discussion of the brightest stars and the nearest stars has given us a good idea of the kinds of stars that exist in space, and Figs. 35 and 36 have shown the relation between absolute magnitude and spectral class for the brightest and the nearest stars. Such an array is known as a *Hertzsprung-Russell diagram,* carrying the names of two of the greatest astronomers of our time.

Figure 37 shows a schematic drawing of the diagram with the main sequence and the giant branches drawn in. This diagram is one that applies to the stars which are thought of as belonging to the sun's neighbors, taken in the larger sense, and spoken of as Population I. These stars are known to be characteristic of the stellar population in the arms of the spiral galaxies, and most of the varieties occur also in the spaces between the arms; Population II, which has a very different spectrum-luminosity diagram, is characteristic of the inner parts of a galaxy, where no spiral structure is present. The division into Population I and Population II was first suggested by Baade from his study of the Andromeda nebula. It seems to be a very significant distinction when it comes to showing how spectral characteristics and peculiarities of motion are related, and it will be vital when we come to discuss the origin of stars and their probable evolution. We note that Population I contains very bright

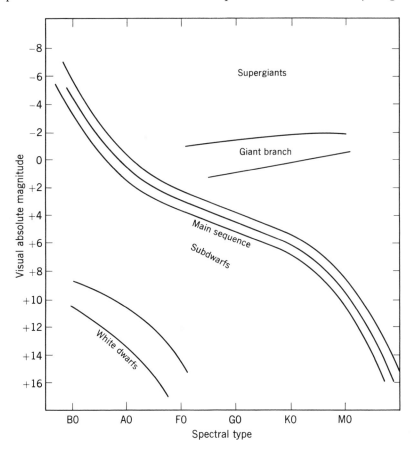

Fig. 37. A schematic Hertzsprung-Russell diagram, giving the names by which the principal varieties of stars of Population I are generally identified.

B stars, supergiants of all classes, the main sequence, and the white dwarfs.

The diagram indicates only the mean values of the absolute magnitudes of the stars. There will be a certain spread about the means in these absolute magnitudes, but in general the stars conform pretty closely to the rules set up by the majority.

*   *

*

The Luminosity Function

We can see from the comparison of the brightest stars and the nearest stars that from these alone we cannot satisfy our desire for completeness both in numbers and in kinds of stars. In our tiny bit of space with a radius of 16 light-years we are fairly complete as to total numbers. But we are totally lacking in the bright B stars and the red giants that are so conspicuous among the brightest stars. If we go to a sufficient distance to include at least some of these, we have such a large volume of space that we are far from having complete information as to just how many other stars it contains.

Yet the astronomer wants to know how many stars of given absolute magnitude and spectral class are present in a given volume of space. It lies within his power to count the stars to given limits of apparent magnitude. Such counts are a task that calls for ingenuity, patience, and skill. But counts alone are not enough. The astronomer does not want to see the sky as all primitive people see it, as a curved surface on which bright lights appear. It is not even enough that he notes more details in his picture of the distribution of the stars. What he must add is the third dimension, so that he can see how the stars are spread out in space. One way to do this is to discover first what a typical sample of space contains. If he assumes that all space contains the same variety of star material in the same proportions, then, working from his distributions in apparent magnitude, he can try to change his surface picture into a space picture.

One of the main objectives of the present chapter is, therefore, to describe how we have succeeded in deriving the complete tabulations of the absolute magnitudes for a typical sample volume in the Milky Way, at least for the parts of the system like that in which our sun is located. This tabulation, which lists the numbers of stars per unit volume for successive intervals of absolute magnitude, is known among astronomers as the *luminosity function*. It is clear that the problem of deriving the luminosity function will have to be tackled piecemeal. We can build up the general luminosity function by studying first the separate tabulations for different spectral classes and then putting them together in true proportions to obtain the total picture. We shall naturally be very curious to find out whether the same mixture of spectral classes holds in different parts of the Milky Way. We know already from our references to the two populations that there will be very marked differences between the central and the outer parts of the galaxy. But how does the function vary with height above the plane, and how does it vary as we go out from our sun in various directions in the plane?

We shall consider first the faint end of the luminosity function, after that the bright end, and then combine the two. Proper motion is a powerful tool for the selection of the nearer stars, with measurable trigonometric parallaxes, from among the stars at large. A star at a distance of 13 light-years and moving at a rate of 20 kilometers per second of linear crosswise motion will have an observed annual proper motion of just about 1 second of arc; about the same proper motion would be observed for a star at 20 light-years distance moving at the rate of 30 kilometers per second. Since the linear crosswise speeds of stars range generally between 5 and 50 kilometers per second, with the majority between 20 and 30 kilometers per second, we may expect the majority of the stars with proper motions of the order of 1 second of arc to have measurable trigonometric parallaxes. Parallax observers naturally concentrate their efforts on varieties of stars that show promise of having measurable trigonometric parallaxes, so it is not surprising that parallax determinations are available for a sizable sample of all known stars with large proper motions. The sample is sufficiently large to permit the use of statistical techniques to correct for the absent stars and make the census figures complete and representative ones. The faint end of the general luminosity function is today fairly well known from an analysis of available data on trigonometric parallaxes for stars with known proper motions in excess of 0.2 second of arc per year. The most complete study of the faint end of the luminosity function has been made in recent years by Luyten of the University of Minnesota.

Trigonometric parallaxes fail us miserably when we attempt to derive the luminosity function for stars with absolute magnitudes like our sun and brighter. For these stars we turn to studies involving proper motions and radial velocities and also to work on the precise determination of spectral types and luminosities. Before we describe the specific application to problems of the luminosity function, we should discuss briefly some basic problems of motions in the vicinity of the sun.

When we spoke of the highest accuracy attainable in the measurement of trigonometric parallaxes, we wished that we could have a longer base line from which to make our measurements. How can we extend our base line? The earth shares the motion of the sun, which is moving with reference to the nearby stars at the rate of 18 to 20 kilometers per second in the direction of the constellation Hercules. Can this displacement of the earth be used to give us different positions from which to measure shifts of the star's positions? If we examine the available radial velocities for the brighter stars, what effect of the *solar motion* do we find?

Figure 38 shows a projection of the sky, so drawn that equal areas on the sphere are equal areas on the paper. The sky has been divided into 94 equal areas. For each of these regions the available radial velocities of the naked-eye stars have been averaged. Altogether the radial velocities of 2149 stars were used, so that in each area there were on the average some 20 stars.

If the sun were at rest and the stars moving at random, there should be roughly as many positive as negative values for the radial velocities and the resultant average should be close to zero in each of the areas. Figure 38 shows what we actually find from the observations. The stars near the circle mark in the upper left-hand part of the figure have an average radial velocity of -20 kilometers per second; those near the asterisk in the lower right-hand part are of the order of $+20$ kilometers per second. Since the negative value indicates approach, it would seem that, as viewed from the sun, all the stars in one part of the sky are marching toward us; in the opposite region they are moving away.

What is to blame, our sun or the stars? So long as we have no fixed landmark we cannot decide that question, but the simpler assumption, of course, is that the effect is the reflex of the sun's motion. With reference to the naked-eye stars, the sun is moving toward a point in the constellation Hercules and not far from the bright star Vega at the rate of 20 kilometers per second. The circle mark in Fig. 38 is called the *apex* of the sun's motion; the asterisk the *antapex*.

At the rate of 20 kilometers per second, in the course of a year

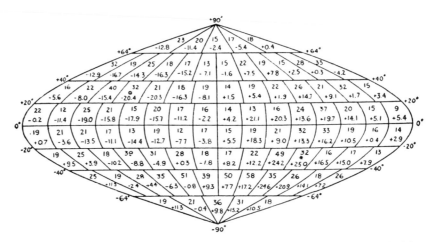

Fig. 38. The sun's motion from radial velocities. Averages of the radial velocities for 2149 naked-eye stars measured at the Lick Observatory. The position of the apex of the sun's motion is shown by a small circle near the position of greatest average negative radial velocity.

of about 31,600,000 seconds, the sun will travel 630,000,000 kilometers, or the equivalent of 4.2 astronomical units per year. Our earth moves steadily along with the sun at the same rate. After an interval of 25 years we are more than 100 astronomical units from our starting place. We can take sights on the stars as we march along and measure their average displacements.

Let us see how the proper motions of the stars are affected by the

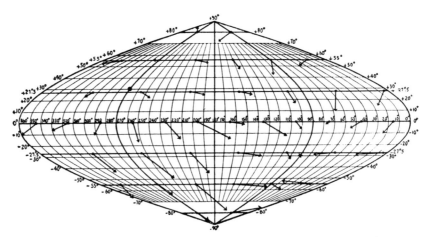

Fig. 39. The sun's motion from proper motions. The arrows represent the average directions and amount of proper motions for 726 A stars of the fifth apparent magnitude.

sun's motion. Figure 39 is the same projection of the sphere that we had in Fig. 38, but this time we have chosen to look into the proper motions of 726 A-type stars of the fifth apparent magnitude. They were divided into 42 groups according to their positions in the sky and for all groups we determined the average proper motions, which are shown by the lengths of the arrows. These arrows are necessarily much too long for the size of the sphere.

You will notice that most of the arrows seem to be pointing away from the solar apex and toward the solar antapex. With respect to the sun, the stars are moving in one direction, or vice versa, our sun is moving in the opposite direction with respect to the A stars.

Since proper motions are angular displacements on the sky, they will tend to be largest along the circle at right angles to the direction in which we are traveling, or, in Fig. 39 along the projection of the circle that falls halfway between the apex and the antapex. The average of these maximum lengths is of the order of 0.040 second of arc per year for the A stars in Fig. 39.

How can we combine this 0.040 second of arc per year with the value, found from the radial velocities, of 20 kilometers per second or 4.2 astronomical units per year? We must remember one outstanding difference between radial velocities and proper motions. Radial velocities do not depend on the distances of the stars. So long as a star is bright enough to appear on a spectrum plate, its radial velocity can be determined in kilometers or miles per second and it matters not at all whether the star is nearby or very distant. Proper motion, on the other hand, varies with the distance, growing smaller as distance increases. The effect of the solar motion on the stars will therefore depend on the average distance of the group of stars under investigation. The effect will be larger for the nearby stars, just as for a train traveler the telegraph poles will appear to whiz past while the distant mountains apparently recede slowly. You see now why we chose the proper motions of a group of A stars all of one apparent magnitude, whereas for the radial velocities we had a wide range of brightness. For the A stars there is not the division into giants and dwarfs that occurs in later-type stars, so that all the A stars of the fifth magnitude will be at about the same distance. What is that average distance?

By definition, the parallax of a star is the angular displacement corresponding to 1 astronomical unit at the distance of the star. We have an angular displacement of 0.40 second of arc per year to which corresponds 4.2 astronomical units at the average distance of the group of stars. The mean parallax for our A stars is therefore equal to 0.040/4.2 = 0.0095 second of arc and their average distance is of the order of 105 parsecs or 340 light-years.

This distance is just beyond the distance for which accurate trigonometric parallaxes can be obtained. We shall have to remember that it is only an average distance and that it may be considerably in error for an individual A star. But it is a reliable average and we can go one step further and compute from it the corresponding average absolute magnitude for our A stars. For a star of apparent magnitude 5.5 at a distance of 105 parsecs, the absolute magnitude can be computed from the formula

$$M = m + 5 - 5 \log d,$$

which gives in our special case

$$M = +0.4$$

as the mean absolute magnitude for our A stars. The average A star in our sample is intrinsically about 50 times as luminous as our sun.

Our method of measuring *mean parallaxes* can be applied to any group with known proper motions, provided that these stars are evenly distributed over the sky. It is still applicable for groups of stars that have an average proper motion of the order of 0.008 second of arc per year and that are, therefore, five times as far away as the A stars in our special example. Radial velocities should be available for enough stars of any particular group that we can check that the solar motion agrees with the usual value found from other groups of stars. If all is well, we can immediately compute a mean parallax, a mean distance, and a mean absolute magnitude. Our method will, however, not produce correct results if, unfortunately, we should select a group that has a peculiar motion of its own.

The method of mean parallaxes has one great advantage over the basic trigonometric method: the total displacement from which the mean parallax is found increases with time. By waiting a longer interval, we can obtain increasingly accurate values for the proper motions and so more reliable mean parallaxes. If the stars are so distant that we do not get a measurable effect in 10 years we can wait 20, 40, or if necessary, 100 years. With the aid of trigonometric parallaxes we cannot reach beyond distances of 200 to 300 light-years, but through the mean parallaxes we can gather information that is still reasonably accurate for distances of 1500 light-years and over. Research on mean parallaxes continues to be of importance for extending our basic scale of distances. In recent years, the most extensive and significant research in this area has been done by A. N. and Emma Williams Vyssotsky at the McCormick Observatory.

Fortunately, we do not have to depend exclusively on the evidence from mean parallaxes for the stars beyond the reach of the trigonometric method. Spectral-luminosity classification is now possible for all stars for which objective-prism spectra of not too low dispersion are obtainable. By careful inspection of the spectra, one may obtain an estimate of any star's absolute magnitude with an uncertainty that need not exceed one-half magnitude. In other words, we can take a fairly accurate star-to-star census and combine the results to derive the distribution function of absolute magnitudes—the luminosity function—per unit volume for all stars of all spectral types taken together.

By a combination of the results of the various methods we can thus obtain reliable data on the distribution of the absolute magnitudes of the stars in the sun's neighborhood. The pioneer investiga-

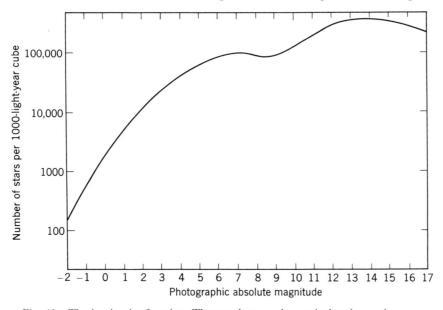

Fig. 40. The luminosity function. The numbers on the vertical scale are the numbers of stars in a cube 1000 light-years on each side for the photographic magnitudes shown on the horizontal scale. (From data compiled by van Rhijn, McCuskey, and Kuiper.)

tions of Kapteyn were followed by extensive studies by Seares and van Rhijn. The method by which we determine at least the bright end of the general luminosity function, by combining the luminosity functions for stars of successive relatively small intervals of spectral class, was first used in 1932 by van Rhijn and Schwassmann. The resulting final curve is shown in Fig. 40 and it represents in a way the combination of two luminosity functions, one derived from proper motions, the other from a combination of separate functions for each spectral class. The curve shown represents the number of stars in a cube 1000 light-years on a side.

The bright end of the general luminosity function has been tested by studies at the Harvard Observatory and, especially in recent years, at the Warner and Swasey Observatory. The work of McCuskey and his associates has not only given a very valuable check of the luminosity function for the regions directly around the sun, but it has further provided useful information regarding the variations in the shape of the function for regions within 500 parsecs of the sun in the galactic plane. McCuskey finds for absolute magnitude -1 to $+1$ somewhat greater numbers of stars per unit volume than shown by the curve of Fig. 40, but on the whole there is little that can be done to improve the original results of van Rhijn and Schwassmann. In the galactic plane, there are fluctuations of the order of 30 percent in the relative frequencies of the various absolute magnitudes.

Marked systematic variations are found if we consider the frequency distributions of absolute magnitudes at some distance from the galactic plane. The absolutely brightest stars—B and A stars, for instance—thin out far more rapidly on a proportional basis than do the G and K dwarfs, and the shape of the luminosity function at 1000 light-years above or below the galactic plane differs markedly from that shown in Fig. 40, the principal difference being a decided deficiency for the brighter absolute magnitudes at some height above or below the plane as compared with the relative numbers in the plane.

The bright end of the luminosity curve is the most important part for the study of the distribution of the stars in space. The dwarfs, however, constitute the bulk of the population. Their luminosities are equal to or less than that of the sun, so that it takes many fainter ones to shine as brightly as the giants. But their masses are not too different from the sun's mass and these faintly shining bodies play an important role in determining the general motions of the system.

4

Reaching Out—
The System Takes Shape

Our Distant Neighbors

In the preceding chapter we made a census of the star population
in a fairly small sample of our galactic system, the region within
two or three hundred light-years of our sun. Armed with this information we now set out to analyze the observations on the distribution of stars in the more remote parts of our Milky Way. We
want to learn the size and extent of the whole galaxy, its shape,
and the sun's position in the system.

It is natural that we should hope to solve this problem through
analysis of complete data on stellar distribution. Unfortunately,
what seemed at one time like a main thoroughfare has turned out
to be a dead-end road. We find that in spite of all available statistical information on the distribution of magnitudes, spectra, colors,
and motions, we cannot penetrate to the heart of our galaxy. We
shall instead have to make use of variable stars, clusters, and distant highly luminous objects, such as novae and planetary nebulae.

First, however, let us investigate the possibilities and the limitations of a wholesale attack through counts of stars and spectra and colors.

The approach that was favored 40 to 50 years ago seemed like a relatively straightforward one. With good sequences of standard magnitudes established over the sky, we would proceed to count for a limited number of areas in the sky—Kapteyn's Selected Areas, for instance—the numbers of stars per square degree of the sky for successive photographic magnitudes down to the seventeenth. As improved standard sequences to faint limits and more powerful telescopes became available, we looked forward to extending such counts, possibly to the twenty-second photographic magnitude. Then, with the aid of the luminosity function as established for the regions around the sun (Chapter 3), we planned to deduce the distribution in depth of the number of stars per unit volume of space; in other words, we expected to find out whether or not the stars would thin out as we proceed in various directions from the sun into the vast space of our galaxy.

For greater precision, we would probably want to make use of statistics based on spectral classification and thus subdivide the stars at each apparent magnitude into groups with a small and fairly well-established range of absolute magnitude. In this case we would obviously have to place the lower limits of our surveys at not too faint apparent magnitudes—presumably somewhere between $m = 12$ and $m = 15$—but we might gain in space-penetrating power by considering certain intrinsically very luminous classes of stars, like the O, B, and A stars.

Why did this fine scheme not reveal the general structure of our galaxy? There are two basic reasons why it failed. One reason was that workers in the field could not know that the general luminosity function of Kapteyn and van Rhijn applies strictly only to the regions immediately near the sun. Since it differs radically for a cube 10 light-years on a side near the sun and for a similar cube at a distance of 10,000 light-years from the sun in the direction of the constellation Sagittarius, the whole basis for analysis breaks down. The second reason for the failure was that interstellar absorption is ever present, and it is quite difficult to estimate the amount for any direction at various distances from the sun. Until 1930 there was very little accepted evidence for interstellar absorption.

Let us first examine rather closely how far out in space we can really obtain information about the shape of the general luminosity

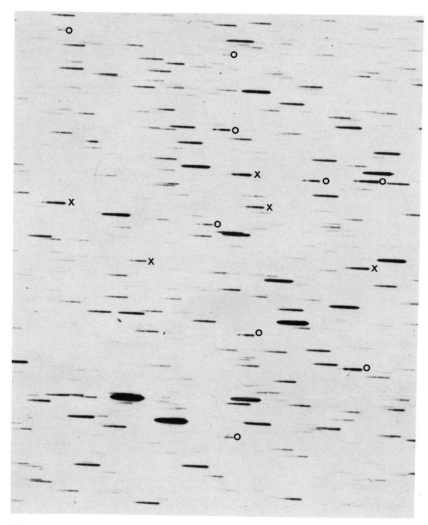

Fig. 41.   A section of an objective-prism spectrum plate in the infrared made with the 4° prism of the Burrell telescope of the Warner and Swasey Observatory. Nassau has indicated by crosses some red stars with spectral classes earlier than M5 and by circles some stars later than M5.

function and changes in that shape. If we limit ourselves to regions at low galactic latitudes (hence close to the galactic plane), as was done in the extensive surveys of McCuskey and associates at the Warner and Swasey Observatory, then we succeed in confirming the reliability of the basic van Rhijn function fairly well to distances up to 5000 light-years from the sun—but definitely not be-

yond. The indications are that for several directions we may expect
to find a radically different distribution at 10,000 light-years from
the sun. In the direction of Sagittarius the distribution function of
absolute magnitudes at 20,000 light-years from the sun probably
bears little resemblance to that for the regions near the sun.

We have available for the Sagittarius section, which marks the
direction toward the center of our system, apart from the regular
material on colors, magnitudes, and spectral types of the brighter
stars, the results of spectral classification in the infrared by Nassau
and associates. Some of the late M-type stars (presumably mostly
giants) show terrific concentrations in the Sagittarius section (Fig.
42). Certain objects, such as planetary nebulae, R R Lyrae variables, Cepheid variables of the W Virginis variety, and novae, which
are rare for the immediate vicinity of our sun, occur in abundance
at great distances in the Sagittarius section. But others, notably faint

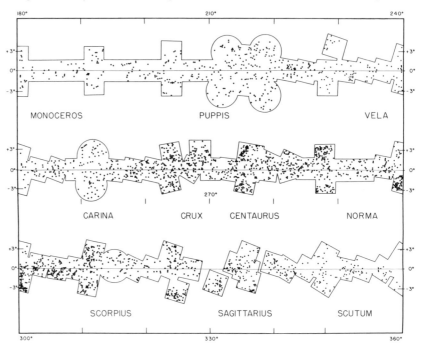

Fig. 42. The distribution in the southern Milky Way of stars of type M5.5 and
later shows a marked concentration from Crux to Sagittarius. The galactic longitudes are shown on the horizontal scales, the latitudes on the vertical scales, and
the relevant constellations are shown as well. The distribution is greatly affected
by dark clouds. The study was made by Elske v. P. Smith and Henry J. Smith at
the Boyden Station.

O and B stars, W stars, emission nebulae, and classical Cepheids are lacking for this same region.

If we refer to the familiar distribution of absolute magnitudes and varieties of objects near the sun as Population I, then we distinguish a very different arrangement at great distances from the sun in the Sagittarius section; following Baade, we refer to this as Population II. Population I, with its abundance of intrinsically very luminous objects is apparently characteristic for the outer parts of our own and other galaxies, whereas Population II prevails in the central cores of galaxies like our own.

The idea that there might be different varieties of stars in different parts of our galaxy did not originate with Baade, but goes back to the 1920's and the early researches on colors and magnitudes of stars in galactic and globular clusters, notably the basic and important work of Shapley and Trumpler, to which we shall return later in this chapter. In the middle thirties several astronomers drew attention to the remarkable relations, particularly those involving stars of high velocity (see Chapter 5), that apparently exist between the physical characteristics of the stars and their velocity characteristics. It was suggested that certain varieties of stars, which move in elongated orbits relative to the galactic center—the RR Lyrae variables, for instance—are a different breed from the normal O, B, and A stars, which move in more or less circular orbits. It is, however, interesting that the realization of a separation between the two major populations came first not as a result of studies of our own galaxy, but rather from Baade's researches on our nearest large neighbor galaxy, Messier 31, the famous Andromeda spiral.

Messier 31 is so far from us—its distance is of the order of 1,600,-000 light-years—that we cannot hope to observe in it stars of faint absolute magnitudes. Even with a very powerful telescope like the Palomar 200-inch, one cannot detect stars as faint as $M = -3$, or 1500 times as bright as the sun. Baade reasoned that it should, however, be possible to find with relative ease anywhere in Messier 31 the stars with absolute magnitudes $M = -4$ and certainly those with $M = -5$ and brighter. If the luminosity function were the same everywhere, then the stars with $M = -4, -5$, and brighter should appear in all parts of the galaxy. Baade showed conclusively that this was not the case. He found it at first impossible to photograph in normal blue light the individual stars in the central regions of Messier 31, whereas in the outer regions, where the spiral arms

TABLE 3. THE BASIC POPULATIONS.

Extreme Population I	Population I	Disk Population	Population II	Extreme Population II
OB stars, clusters, and associations	Normal A to F stars	G to K main sequence	Long-period variables ($P = 200$ to 50 days)	Globular clusters
Wolf Rayet stars	Red supergiants	G to K normal giants	W Virginis Cepheids	RR Lyrae clusters
Hα emission nebulae	Galactic clusters (*not* with OB stars)	Long-period variables ($P > 300$ days)	Planetary nebulae	Subdwarfs
Classical Cepheids	Novae (?)	Semiregular variables	Weak-line stars	High-velocity stars ($V > 100$ km/sec)
Cosmic dust			White dwarfs	
Neutral hydrogen (21-cm radiation)				

appear, the individual stars and groups of stars were clearly shown. With the aid of red-sensitive photographic plates, the nucleus of Messier 31 and the accompanying elliptical galaxy, known as NGC 205, were resolved into stars, the brightest of which proved to be red stars with visual absolute magnitudes between $M = -3.5$ and -4.0 and with color indices of the order of one magnitude and greater.

Baade concluded from these observations that the stars that populate the nucleus are very different (Population II) from those that are found in the outer spiral regions (Population I). The contrast between the two populations is not a minor one; the brightest stars in Population I are blue and have absolute magnitudes of the order of -7 or -8, whereas the brightest stars of Population II are red and have absolute magnitudes of -3 at the brightest. Moreover, interstellar gas and dust abound in Population I, whereas in Population II gas and dust are absent or are minor constituents. The distinction between the two populations represents a major advance in the understanding of our own and other galaxies. We shall have to refer to it time and again, for not only does it possess tremendous significance for the study of the structure of galaxies, but the population approach has far-reaching consequences for theories of stellar birth and evolution.

In the present book we shall, for reasons of simplicity, refer mostly to the two basic populations. The reader should be warned, however, that the picture of two essentially different varieties of stars is an oversimplification. It is true that it seems to be supported by the spiral-galaxy data, but here we are dealing always with stars that are at least five absolute magnitudes brighter than our sun; even our best equipment does not permit us to observe the common stars of moderate absolute magnitude. The authors—and along with them quite a few of their colleagues—prefer to think in terms of at least three basic varieties of stars: Population I, responsible for the principal spectacular spiral features; the Common Stars, first so named by Oort, which inhabit the more or less amorphous regions between the spiral arms; and Population II, the nuclear population, which spills over to some extent into the inner outer parts.

Perhaps it is more fitting to think in terms of five major groupings, somewhat in the manner of Table 3. Extreme Population I refers here to the objects that show very marked preference for association with the spiral features. Under Population I we refer to objects that occur in or near the spiral features and that are generally found close to the central plane of our galaxy, though they need not follow precisely the dominant spiral pattern. Thirdly, we have the Disk Population, the Common Stars of Oort, which are the major contributors to the amorphous interarm regions. Finally, we distinguish between Population II stars, which show preference for the nuclear part of our galaxy and still show some concentration to the galactic plane, and the Extreme Population II objects, which are found either within very small distances of the center of the galaxy, or else in the outer halo of our galaxy, distributed without much, if any, concentration to the central plane.

An even more extreme point of view is taken by Parenago, Kukarkin, and others among the leading astronomers of the Soviet Union, who consider it unlikely that it is feasible to talk in terms of separate populations and argue in favor of a smooth gradation in which there exists a continuous sequence of groupings of stars by their physical characteristics and motions into separate subsystems of our galaxy. The Soviet astronomers have all along been the strongest supporters of a minimum of three major subdivisions: a highly flattened, an intermediate, and a roughly spherical component.

*   *

*

Galactic Clusters

On any clear night we notice, apart from the general hit-or-miss arrangement of the stars, a few places where the stars are closely

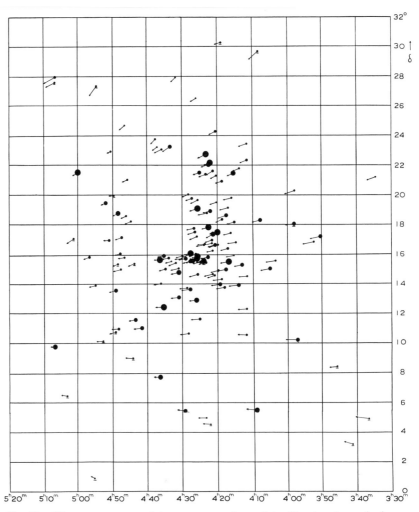

Fig. 43.   The convergence of the proper motions of the Hyades cluster is shown
by this diagram. All stars brighter than the ninth magnitude belonging to the
cluster have been mapped. The sizes of the dots are a measure of the magnitudes
of the stars. The arrows show the proper-motion displacements that may be expected in the course of the next 18,000 years. It is apparent that the stars share
a common motion in space. This figure is by van Bueren, who made the study at
the Leiden Observatory.

clustered and seem to belong together. The Pleiades, or Seven Sisters, the Praesepe or Beehive cluster, the Hyades in Taurus, the Double Cluster *h* and Chi Persei—these have all been known since antiquity. To these naked-eye clusters, telescopic surveys have added many more.

The stars of a galactic cluster are close together in space, not merely a chance arrangement. If a cluster is real and has some lasting quality, all its stars should share a common motion. They should, therefore, move through space in parallel paths, and with identical speeds. If the group covers a large area of the sky—as do, for example, the Hyades—the arrows that represent the directions of motion of individual stars in one cluster will all seem to converge on one distant point on the celestial sphere, just as the rails of a straight stretch of railroad track seem to meet on the horizon. We generally refer to the galactic clusters that are close enough to us to show a measurable proper motion as *moving clusters*. The Hyades are the prototype of a moving cluster.

Lewis Boss first detected the convergent motion for the Hyades when he was preparing his catalogue of proper motions. For this cluster the proper motion is large, and it is possible to sort out accurately the stars that belong to the cluster from among the field stars (Fig. 43). Since the distance can be measured, it is possible to build up a picture of the cluster, discover the kind of stars it contains, and find how closely they are packed. Van Bueren has made the most complete recent study of the Hyades cluster, which he finds to be a flattened system with its shortest axis perpendicular to the galactic plane and about two-thirds as long as the long axis in the plane. The cluster is nearby—only 130 light-years, or about 40 parsecs, from the sun—and van Bueren has listed and classified all of its members from the brightest to stars fainter than our sun. The stars are concentrated toward the center of the cluster, though in a somewhat irregular fashion. The majority of the cluster members are G- and K-type main-sequence stars. The bluest stars in the cluster are of spectral type A2 and there are a very few G- and K-type giants. In the core of the cluster the average density of stars is at least three times the average density for the region around the sun.

The total number of moving clusters is small, since almost all galactic clusters are so far away that they do not show measurable proper motion. But in spite of the absence of observable motion we

Fig. 44. The Pleiades cluster. The Pleiades are embedded in nebulosity. (From a photograph by Barnard.)

can learn much about the more distant galactic clusters. Some are rich in numbers of stars, others are little more than slight condensations in the sky. After omitting the globular clusters, we are left with some 400 clusters that are strictly galactic or open clusters. The majority are located close to or in the band of the Milky Way. There are probably many more than 400 in our Milky Way system, but the more distant clusters are not noticed in the rich stellar background along the Milky Way. The cataloging of galactic clusters continues to be a major task facing astronomers. The most recent extensive atlas has been prepared by Markarian of the

Burakan Observatory. The search for new galactic clusters is by no means completed, especially for the Southern Hemisphere.

Much has been learned about distances and physical characteristics of galactic clusters from the classification of the spectral types of the member stars. The most significant early research in this field was done in the late 1920's by Trumpler and by Shapley. In 1930, Trumpler summarized his researches in a paper published in a *Lick Observatory Bulletin* which today stands out as a classic of its time. Both he and Shapley stressed the striking differences in spectral composition for some of the better-known clusters, and they intimated—as since has been proved to be so significant—that these differences might well have great importance for problems of stellar evolution. From Trumpler's study, there came the first conclusive proof of the presence of interstellar absorption at low galactic latitudes. We should note here that the first relevant observations for the law of space reddening followed also from studies by Trumpler on the intensity distribution of the continuum in the spectra of some heavily obscured distant stars. The early, rather crude, system of spectral classification has now been superseded by the more sophisticated system of spectrum-luminosity classification developed by Morgan, Keenan, and Kellman. Modern photoelectric photometry enables us to measure with great precision the colors and probable color excesses of the cluster members. In spite of these recent developments, the early work in the field continues to stand as one of the major contributions to the understanding of our galaxy.

During the 1930's, it became evident that much of value was to be learned from the Hertzsprung-Russell diagrams (generally referred to in the professional vernacular as the H-R diagrams) of galactic clusters. There are two ways in which the H-R diagram can be plotted. The first method is to plot spectral class (horizontally) against apparent or absolute magnitude (vertically). In the second method, the measured color index of each individual cluster star replaces the spectral type. Now that it is possible by photoelectric techniques to measure color indices of faint stars quickly and precisely, the second variety has become the more popular.

Figure 45 shows a composite H-R diagram in which the principal branches of the color-magnitude arrays are plotted for some of the best-known clusters. In the diagram we find vertically the absolute visual magnitude M_v, and horizontally the color index, defined as the difference between the blue magnitude B and the visual

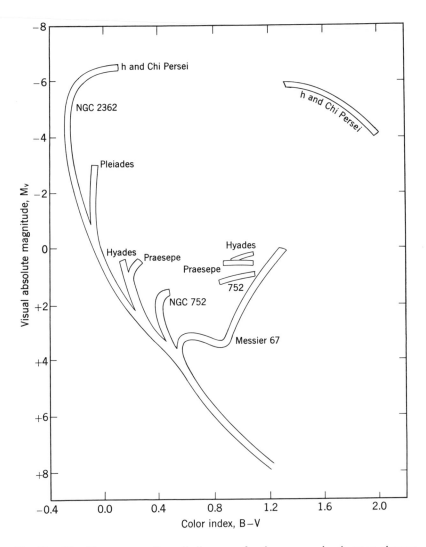

Fig. 45.   The Hertzsprung-Russell diagrams for the seven galactic open clusters *h* and Chi Persei, NGC 2362, the Pleiades, the Hyades, Praesepe, NGC 752, and Messier 67 have been combined in this diagram by Harold Johnson and Sandage. The main sequences of the clusters converge toward the faint end but there are great differences in the upper regions of the main sequence and in the giant and supergiant branches.

magnitude V. Upon inspection, we note that the Hyades cluster falls somewhere near the middle of the diagram and that it and Praesepe are rather similar in that they have no really blue stars and no stars as bright as absolute magnitude $M_v = 0$, that is, no stars as much as 100 times as bright as our sun. In other words, these clusters contain a few mild giant stars, but they have no blue giants and certainly no supergiants among their members. Let us now examine some of the clusters that occupy the upper left-hand section of Fig. 45. Here we find some familiar star clusters, the Pleiades and the Double Cluster h and Chi Persei. The Pleiades cluster has a steep blue branch, with some stars reaching $M_v = -2.5$, that is, 1000 times the brightness of our sun. The cluster h and Chi Persei outdoes all others, with blue supergiants and a few red ones at $M_v = -6$, fully 25,000 times as bright intrinsically as our sun! But, turning to the lower half of the diagram, we find some inconspicuous clusters like Messier 67 in which the bluest star is hardly bluer or brighter than our own sun, which in this particular diagram would be located at the point $B - V = +0.5$, $M_v = +5$.

There are two reasons why diagrams like those shown in Fig. 45 are of great interest to the astronomer. The first is that the information contained is helpful in the study of the distances of remote galactic clusters; the second is that from diagrams of this nature we may learn much about the ways in which the stars gradually evolve. We shall concern ourselves briefly with these two problems.

With the exception of not more than half a dozen nearby clusters, the distances of the remaining several hundred galactic clusters are too great to be measured by either the trigonometric or the moving-cluster technique. But it is possible to measure, by a combination of photographic and photoelectric techniques, the colors and magnitudes of very faint stars in galactic clusters. If one so desires, it is quite feasible to establish the color-magnitude array for a hundred or more galactic clusters. In every case one will end up with a diagram in which observed color (such as $B - V$ in Fig. 45) is plotted against the apparent magnitude m_v of each cluster star. One may then draw through the observed points the best-fitting curve and attempt to judge by inspection to which curve in Fig. 45 it corresponds. It is generally not difficult to decide whether the cluster one is dealing with is like the Pleiades, h and Chi Persei, the Hyades or Praesepe, or is an extreme case like Messier 67. In the absence of any appreciable interstellar absorption, the procedure of finding the distance to the cluster is then simple and direct: one simply notes at various values of $B - V$ the corresponding values of M_v from Fig. 45 and the observed values of m_v. The two quantities —absolute and apparent magnitude—are related through the basic equation of Chapter 2, applied to visual magnitudes,

$$M_v = m_v + 5 - 5 \log d,$$

and from this relation one derives directly the logarithm of the distance, in parsecs, from our sun and earth to the cluster. To check the resulting distance, one should attempt to obtain, if possible, the spectral type on the Morgan-Keenan system for the brightest members. From these spectral types *and* luminosity classes we can readily check on the absolute magnitudes M_v of some of the individual bright stars, and thus on the distance. A few well-determined spectral types and luminosity classes help immeasurably in disentangling the complex situations that often arise in practice.

Interstellar absorption and the accompanying reddening, which affects the observed colors $B - V$, complicate matters considerably, but with some care the distance problem is still amenable to relatively straightforward handling. It is simplest when the spectral types and luminosity classes are available for a few of the brighter members of the cluster. From the spectral data one can then predict for each star the intrinsic value of $B - V$ and derive the amount of reddening by noting the difference between it and the observed value of $B - V$ for the same star; we call this difference the *color excess*. From the scattering and absorbing properties of the interstellar medium (see Chapter 7), we know fairly well what is the value of the factor by which we must multiply the color excess to obtain the corresponding total photographic or visual absorption; for $B - V$ color excesses the factors are approximately 5 and 4. Multiplication by this factor then yields the total photovisual absorption between the star in the cluster and the sun and earth. If we call this absorption A_v, then the relation between the relevant quantities reads simply

$$M_v = m_v + 5 - 5 \log d - A_v,$$

and again we know every quantity with the exception of d, the distance of the cluster. If no spectral data are available at all, one can often make a good guess at the absorption by noting precisely where the most marked kinks occur in the observed arrays of $B - V$ versus apparent magnitude m_v.

Close to 400 galactic clusters have been recognized on our Milky Way photographs. The required basic information on apparent magnitudes, colors, spectral types, and luminosity classes is available for hardly more than 10 percent of this total, and much of this material is of a rather heterogeneous nature. The great majority of the galactic clusters studied to date lie within 10,000 light-years of our sun and the remaining ones with known distances are almost all within 15,000 light-years of our sun. The clusters are almost all less than 500 light-years from the central galactic plane. In other words, in our disklike Milky Way system they occur apparently most often in a belt near the central plane, the band in which—as we shall see in subsequent chapters—spiral structure prevails. Galactic star clusters have a distribution that is totally different from that of the globular star clusters, which inhabit the central regions of our galaxy, or are found at great distances from the galactic plane, and seem to avoid the outer belt of spiral structure. Galactic clusters belong for the greater part to Population I, whereas the globular clusters are of Population II.

It is obviously important that we should learn more about the distribution in space of the 90 percent or so of the known galactic clusters with poorly determined distances. The most direct solution of this problem is through studies of colors and magnitudes. Here the photoelectric technique should be basic, but it may—and often must—be supplemented by photographic observations. The photoelectric observations yield a limited number of precise standards of colors and magnitudes, especially in the thin outer parts of a cluster. With the aid of what we may call "photographic interpolation," we can then determine colors and magnitudes for a hundred or more stars by measuring their magnitudes in two or three colors with reference to the standard stars.

There are several methods in vogue for research of this sort, one of the most useful of these being that developed by W. Becker of Basel, who measures his magnitudes in three carefully selected wavelength intervals and then succeeds in a straightforward manner in separating effects of space reddening from those produced by the intrinsic colors of the stars. Becker's method holds great promise for future development and should yield rather promptly the detailed outline of the system of the galactic clusters. It seems likely that the photoelectric method itself will be developed in the next few years to such an extent that it by itself will produce reliable color data for faint stars in remote galactic clusters. In this area the researches of Strömgren and associates at the Yerkes Observatory and at Copenhagen hold the greatest promise for future development. By a skillful selection of a series of narrow-band color filters, Strömgren has succeeded in deriving for very faint stars intrinsic colors that are sufficiently accurate to permit the derivation from them alone of spectral types and luminosity classes.

Twenty or so years ago, many astronomers thought that distance estimates of galactic clusters could be made from studies of apparent diameters of clusters, or from measured magnitudes of the fifth or tenth brightest star of a cluster, or from the total magnitude of a cluster as a whole. Unfortunately, the spread in true linear diameters of galactic clusters is very great and the range in integrated magnitude or in the magnitude of the fifth or tenth brightest star is also so great that these earlier methods appear now to be of little value. Precise determinations of spectral types and luminosity classes, supplemented by extensive measurements of colors and magnitudes, offer for the present the only feasible way of arriving at a true picture of the detailed distribution of galactic clusters in our Milky Way system.

In conclusion, we turn briefly to the problem of the probable evolutionary significance of the observed color-magnitude arrays for galactic clusters. In Fig. 45 we plotted the absolute visual magnitude M_v vertically against the observed color index $B - V$ horizontally. In Fig. 46(a) we have a slightly different version of the

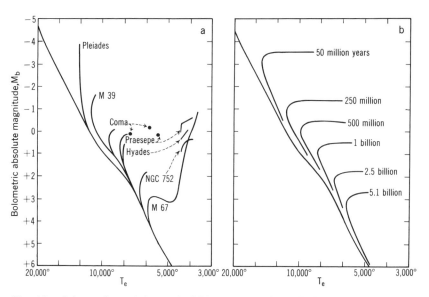

Fig. 46.   Schematic and theoretical Hertzsprung-Russell diagrams for galactic clusters. The two diagrams were published side by side by Oke in the *Journal of the Royal Astronomical Society of Canada 49*, 13 (1955). In (a) the bolometric absolute magnitudes are plotted against the logarithms of the effective temperatures of the stars. In (b) the theoretically predicted diagrams are drawn for star clusters of various ages (see text).

same diagram, in which the *bolometric* absolute magnitude M_b, which includes radiation of all wavelengths, is plotted against the effective temperature T_e at the surface of each star. In Fig. 46(b) we have a diagram of an entirely theoretical nature. It is based upon calculations by Sandage and Schwarzschild. They assumed that at their "birth" all stars of a galactic cluster would be located upon the main-sequence line that runs diagonally down from left to right in the diagram. We shall see later in this book—notably in Chapter 10—that the stars derive their energy of radiation from the continual building up of helium nuclei from hydrogen nuclei and that initially the stars would all remain close to the original main sequence. The intrinsically brightest stars—in the upper left-hand part of the diagram—will exhaust their hydrogen supply the quickest and, as the calculations of Sandage and Schwarzschild show, they will move rapidly to the right in the diagram (still later they will really go down in brightness and end up in all likelihood as hydrogen-poor stars of low luminosity). After 50,000,000 years, there will be no stars brighter than $M_b = -0.5$! From a comparison of Figs. 45 and 46 one may therefore deduce that the Pleiades are no older than 50,000,000 years, that h and Chi Persei are even younger, and that the Hyades may well have existed for something of the order of 1 billion (10^9) years.

No astronomer would contend that with Figs. 45 and 46 the last word has been said about stellar evolution and galactic clusters. But already it is clear that one of the reasons why we should continue to press for more and more precise data on colors and magnitudes in galactic clusters is that from data of this sort, relating presumably to stars formed simultaneously, we may hope to learn much about the probable processes of stellar evolution. We shall return to the subject again in the concluding chapter.

*   *

*

Associations and Aggregates

In addition to the tightly knit clusters of stars there are more loosely connected distant groupings known as *stellar associations* and *aggregates*. For many years astronomers have been aware of the existence of a few very extended moving clusters—the Scorpio-Centaurus cluster of B stars, for instance—recognized by their common space motions. The Russian astronomer Ambartsumian was the first to

Fig. 47. The Horsehead Nebula in Orion (*S* of the star Zeta Orionis) photographed in red light with the 200-inch Hale reflector.

demonstrate that there exist a considerable number of loose group-ings, which he called associations, and which are too distant to show detectable parallelism of proper motions. These occur espe-cially among the very luminous—and presumably very young—O and early B stars. The mutual gravitational attraction between the stars is too small to hold them permanently together, but they have not existed long enough to have been torn asunder by the forces of the Milky Way or to have drifted apart owing to their individual motions. These associations have been studied primarily by Am-bartsumian in the Soviet Union and by Morgan at the Yerkes Observatory and their associates.

The familiar Orion region, with its bright and dark nebulae and an abundance of O and B stars, has several associations, which has led Morgan to refer to it as an aggregate.

Every amateur astronomer is familiar with the beautiful Orion nebula and the associated Trapezium cluster. The nebula itself is a large cloud of ionized hydrogen gas made luminous by the ultra-violet radiation emitted by the hot stars of the Trapezium cluster.

In the same general region of the sky, one finds a very loose grouping of O and B stars, slightly elongated in shape, and extending over a far greater volume of space. Radio observations by Menon at the Agassiz Station have revealed that all these features are imbedded in a very large cloud of neutral hydrogen with a diameter of the order of 300 light-years and with a total mass of the order of 50,000 to 100,000 solar masses; the famous Orion nebula, with a total mass probably no greater than 1000 solar masses, is just a little sore spot of ionized hydrogen in the larger complex. Within this complex are several well-known gaseous and dust features, notably the Horsehead nebula, a beautiful sight when photographed with the 200-inch Hale reflector (Fig. 47). One of the most striking features is a faint arch of nebulosity, first photographed by Barnard. It represents radiation from ionized hydrogen and is apparently formed at the edge of the expanding large neutral gas cloud, possibly by a shock-wave phenomenon that occurs as the huge expanding gas mass (expanding, according to Menon, at the rate of about 10 kilometers per second) bumps into the surrounding interstellar matter. In an extensive study of the Orion aggregate, Parenago has found evidence for a rotation of the entire system of stars and nebulosity. The radio observations of Menon confirm the presence of this rotation. We thus see the Orion aggregate as an enormous interstellar boiling pot, mostly neutral hydrogen gas, some of it apparently condensed into relatively young stars, which ionize some of the gas and cause it to shine. Interstellar dust is sprinkled liberally throughout the complex.

Blaauw has made a remarkable discovery of the expansion of certain associations. For 17 stars near Zeta Persei, all within 100 light-years of each other, he found that proper motions and radial velocities indicate an expansion of the association at an average rate of 12 kilometers per second (Fig. 48). The group would at this rate have expanded to its present size in 1,300,000 years. This interval represents a very short time astronomically speaking, but it is highly suggestive that the age of the whole system is of that order. While at first we may be startled at the shortness of the time, we cannot help but be pleased that the ages of the hottest O and B stars in this association are probably much the same, thus suggesting some sort of explosion a little more than a million years ago in which the stars were produced and then shot out into space.

Blaauw and Morgan have studied other associations in similar

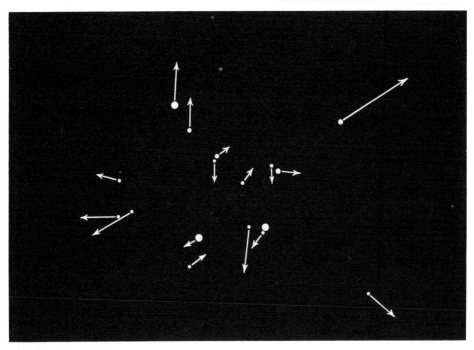

Fig. 48. An expanding association. The figure shows the Zeta Persei association with the arrows indicating the directions in which the stars are traveling and the distances they will cover during the next 500,000 years. The motions of this group have been studied by Blaauw. (Courtesy of *Scientific American*.)

fashion. For a group of about 30 stars near the O-type star 10 Lacertae they find a rate of expansion indicated of the order of 8 kilometers per second, suggesting a probable age of the order of 4,200,000 years. According to Blaauw, there is evidence that the Scorpio-Centaurus moving cluster is an expanding association, with the slow expansion rate of only 0.7 kilometer per second. This gives a probable age of 70,000,000 years, which seems in line with the fact that the Scorpio-Centaurus cluster does not contain excessively luminous, very hot, and hence very young O and B stars, but seems to specialize in the more sedate and older varieties of B stars.

By far the most spectacular expansion phenomenon has been observed by Blaauw and Morgan in connection with the Orion aggregate. The three stars AE Aurigae, Mu Colombae, and 53 Arietis have motions that seem to carry them away from the center of the Orion aggregate at rates in excess of 100 kilometers per second (Fig. 49). They appear to be the hottest and the fastest pellets shot into space by the big Orion explosion of 2,500,000 years ago.

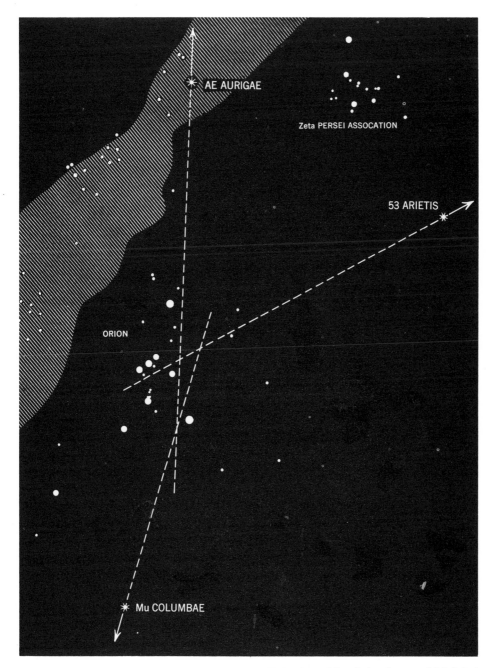

Fig. 49.   Runaway stars from Orion. The stars AE Aurigae, Mu Columbae, and 53 Arietis are fast-moving stars. When their paths are retraced they are found to intersect in the constellation of Orion. It is assumed that they originated in the bright O-association and have erupted from it. (Diagram by Blaauw and Morgan, courtesy of *Scientific American*.)

O and B stars are not the only variety of stars occurring in associations and aggregates. The T associations, discovered and named by Ambartsumian, contain an abundance of the T Tauri-type variable stars. These irregular variable stars are commonly found especially at the edges of very obscured regions. They are probably faint dwarfs and can be recognized either by their variability in light or by bright-line features in their spectra. They occur in groupings, some of them near O–B associations, others by themselves, but always in regions of the sky where cosmic dust is plentiful. In addition to the Soviet astronomers, Haro at the Tonanzintla Observatory in Mexico and Herbig at the Lick Observatory have searched for and studied the T associations. Holopov in the Soviet Union has cataloged the principal T associations and he has noted that the T Tauri variable stars are found especially at the edges of dark nebulae.

The Orion Nebula and surroundings are a T Association. Apart from the many emission objects discovered in and near the Orion nebulosity, there is an abundance of irregularly varying stars, especially in the regions of dark nebulosity. Originally, many astronomers were inclined to consider seriously the hypothesis that these variations might be caused by variable thickness in the obscuring clouds passing over these stars. Parenago has disproved this hypothesis. The fact that many of the variables have emission lines in their spectra, in spite of rather faint absolute magnitudes, suggests that the cause of the variability and the emission features lies either in the star's atmosphere or, possibly, in its interaction with the surrounding cosmic dust and associated interstellar gas. Ambartsumian is of the opinion that the T Tauri variable stars are young stars, formed quite recently from the surrounding dust and gas clouds, but that their variability and the presence of emission lines are effects caused by internal disturbances in these youthful stars rather than by interaction phenomena between the stars and the interstellar clouds. Haro and Herbig find support for this suggestion in the presence of excessive ultraviolet radiation in the spectra of most objects. Herbig has some photographs which suggest that in one or two cases we may actually have observed a new star in the process of formation.

*   *

*

Among the stars that vary in brightness, some do so because they *Pulsating* are changing in size; the star is alternately expanding and con- *Stars* tracting. The periods of light variation range from 80 minutes to over 100 days, but each star retains its own period unchanged. The brightest star of this class is the star Delta of the constellation Cepheus, from which these stars received the name of *Cepheids*. Delta Cephei is an easily identified star, and if it is closely observed for a week or two it is seen to change its brightness between the third and fourth magnitudes in a regular pattern, repeating itself every 5 days 9 hours. Figure 50 shows the light curve; the time is plotted along the horizontal scale and the magnitude along the vertical. This curve shows that Delta Cephei rises quickly to its greatest brilliance, fading away more slowly. Over and over again, unvaryingly, it repeats this pattern of changing brightness.

Together with the change in luminosity occurs a change in color so that the star becomes redder as it becomes fainter. With the aid of the spectrograph the radial velocity is found to vary with the same period as the change in brightness. This variable radial veloc- ity is interpreted as originating from a periodic swelling and shrinking of the star, a real *pulsation*. The time of greatest velocity of approach comes generally at or near the time of maximum light and the greatest velocity of recession comes at or near the time of minimum. The pulsation theory was first advocated by Shapley to explain the behavior of these stars. This theory was developed by Eddington, and later Schwarzschild showed that in addition to the standing waves in the main body of the star, running waves appear near the surface.

While a wide range of periods has been observed, certain periods are favored. Many of these stars have periods of nearly a week or

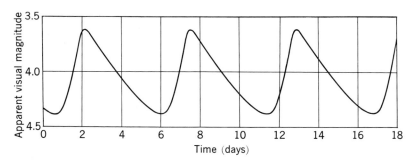

Fig. 50.   Light curve of Delta Cephei. The diagram illustrates the changes in ap- parent magnitude. The period of the light variation is 5 days 9 hours.

slightly longer. There are, however, fainter stars in the sky that also wink on and off but in shorter periods, of about half a day (Fig. 51). The short-period Cepheids are frequently called "cluster variables," because Bailey at Harvard first found that they are present in many globular clusters. We shall prefer to call them RR Lyrae stars after their brightest member.

When we collect the RR Lyrae stars in one group and the pulsating stars of longer period in another group, we find certain other characteristics by which we may distinguish between the two groups. They may be alike in the fact that they are pulsating stars but they differ in other important respects. The longer-period or classical Cepheids are mostly at low galactic latitudes and are slow-moving bodies; both their proper motions and their radial velocities are small. The RR Lyrae stars, on the other hand, move rapidly and are found scattered over the sky and not clinging to the plane of the Milky Way. Here is a warning that they are different sorts of objects—probably different in origin and in age; we must not treat them as members of one single homogeneous group.

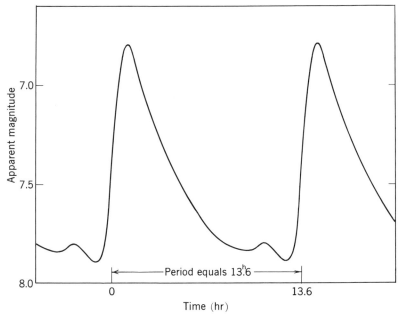

Fig. 51.   A sample light curve of RR Lyrae. The period of this rapidly varying star is 0.567 day = 13.6 hours; its range in brightness is 1.1 magnitudes. The star shows secondary changes in brightness, which cause small periodic changes in the shape of the light curve. (From data assembled by Walraven at Leiden Observatory.)

The RR Lyrae stars are one of the most characteristic varieties of stars of Population II. They are the sort of stars that inhabit the thin outer halo of a galaxy and the central nucleus, but they avoid the central disk of a galaxy and the regions of spiral structure. The long-period Cepheids that we observe most readily belong to Population I, but here we must be careful, for there exist also long-period variable stars with light curves that differ not too much from those of the regular Cepheids, but with different mean absolute magnitudes and with characteristics of Population II objects.

During the past 50 years, the pulsating variables have played an important though rather controversial role in the drama of our unfolding knowledge of the outline and dimensions of the universe of galaxies. The first act opened in 1910, when Miss Leavitt of the Harvard Observatory studied the variable stars in the Small Magellanic Cloud. Their periods varied from a few days to over 100 days. She found a very important relation between the periods and the average brightnesses: the longer the period, the brighter the star appeared on the average.

Hertzsprung, and later Shapley, recognized this relation as being an intrinsic quality of the stars. Since the Magellanic Clouds are systems of very faint stars, they must be very far away. Since the thicknesses of the clouds are very small as compared with their distance, all the stars in them may be assumed to be equally distant, and the relation between the period and the apparent magnitudes will really be one between period and absolute magnitude. The difficulty is to find the constant, or modulus, that must be subtracted from all apparent magnitudes in order to change them to absolute magnitudes.

If we only knew the absolute magnitude of a single Cepheid of known period, we could use it to determine the zero point of the period-luminosity curve, and then the curve might be used to give the absolute magnitude of any Cepheid whose period could be observed. The nearest galactic Cepheids are too distant for accurate measurement of their trigonometric parallaxes. It is necessary to determine the average parallaxes from the proper motions by the method of mean parallaxes described in Chapter 3. But the motions of the stars are small and their distribution over the sky is not uniform. Both factors introduce uncertainties in the parallax determinations, but it was quite clear that even the brightest Cepheids are very distant and highly luminous. Since the RR Lyrae stars show higher velocities, they are especially suited for studies of mean parallaxes. The average radial velocity of a long-period Cepheid variable will generally not exceed 20 kilometers per second, but for the RR Lyrae stars velocities of the order of 100 kilometers per second are by no means uncommon. The high linear velocities lead to average proper motions for the RR Lyrae variables of the tenth magnitude and brighter that are far larger than those of the longer-period Cepheids. The larger size of the proper motions then makes possible fairly accurate determinations of the mean parallaxes for the RR Lyrae variables.

The mean absolute magnitude of the RR Lyrae variables has consistently come out close to $M = 0.0$ on both the photographic and the visual scales. Over the years, it has been suggested that this figure might be in error by as much as half a magnitude, but astronomers have generally seen no reason for accepting a value different from that suggested long ago by Shapley. Since, as we shall see below, the assumed mean absolute magnitude for the RR Lyrae variables is the basic one from which the distances to the globular clusters and to the center of the galaxy are derived, there have been no unexpected large changes in our estimates of these distances. One should, however, bear in mind the continuing possibility that in the future a small correction—possibly as high as half a magnitude—may have to be applied. But whereas the situation seems quite clear for the RR Lyrae variables, the same is not the case for the long-period Cepheids.

Until the late 1940's it was assumed that a single period-luminosity curve could include both the RR Lyrae variables and the classical longer-period Cepheids. The zero point for calibration to absolute magnitude was found by assuming that the apparent magnitude extrapolated by extending the observed curve to periods of the order of a day was to correspond to the absolute magnitude of the RR Lyrae variables, that is, to $M = 0.0$. There was some uneasiness expressed about the fact that Shapley and his associates had never been able to discover any RR Lyrae variables in the Magellanic Clouds, but few were ready to suggest from this negative observation alone that it is not permissible to extend the period-luminosity curve as indicated. Very few astronomers noted a paper published by Mineur in France (1944) in which, from a study of motions, he suggested $M = 0.0$ as a good value for the RR Lyrae variables, but recommended a correction of -1.5 magnitudes to the accepted zero point of the long-period Cepheids.

The question became an acute one about 1950, when Baade was unable to detect the RR Lyrae variables in the Andromeda spiral galaxy. Regular long-period Cepheids had been discovered in abundance by Hubble 25 years earlier and, on the basis of the accepted period-luminosity relation, the distance to the spiral galaxy had been determined. On the basis of this distance, the RR Lyrae variables should be observed in abundance at about $m = 22$, a figure close to, but still well above, the brightness limit for the 200-inch Hale reflector. Baade did not find the RR Lyrae variables as expected and he concluded rightly that the zero point of the period-luminosity relation for the long-period Cepheids required a correction of just about the amount suggested by Mineur. He recognized, moreover, that the few long-period Cepheids observed in globular clusters were a different brand from the majority of those observed nearby in our own galaxy or in the Andromeda galaxy; the globular-cluster variety of long-period Cepheids is Population II (as are the RR Lyrae variables), whereas the regular long-period Cepheids like Delta Cephei and the stars found in the Andromeda galaxy are Population I. We are now prepared to deal with two period-luminosity relations, one for Population I, another for Population II, the relative shift in zero for the two parallel curves being of the order of 1.5 magnitudes, the Population I objects being the brighter (Fig. 52).

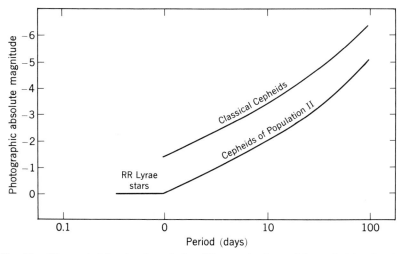

Fig. 52.   The period-luminosity relation. The precise form of the period-luminosity relation is still in doubt, but there is strong evidence to show that the curve for the classical Cepheids lies approximately 1.5 magnitudes brighter than that for the Population II Cepheids.

Two final comments are in order. The first is that a correction of 1.5 magnitudes is no small matter; it means doubling the scales of distance and diameter for all objects whose distances were determined with the aid of the older, erroneous curve. In other words, the distances found before 1950 for galaxies outside our own are probably underestimated by a factor 2 and our own galaxy escaped revision of its distance estimates only because the RR Lyrae variables were basic in establishing its scale.

The second comment is that one must not suppose that the last word has been said in this matter. Some of the Soviet astronomers, notably Kukarkin, have suggested that the correction to the older zero point is more nearly 1.0 than 1.5 magnitudes and they, as well as Arp at Mount Wilson and Palomar, have expressed the opinion that for the long-period Cepheids there may well be more than one period-luminosity relation, especially for Population II.

*   *

*

The System of Globular Clusters   Whereas there are at most two or three thousand stars in a rich galactic cluster, a globular star cluster may contain as many as 100,000 stars. There are 100 known globular clusters in the sky and, unlike the galactic clusters, we do not believe that more than another hundred lie hidden from us. The globular clusters appear in all galactic latitudes and therefore they are not so often veiled by obscuring matter and their concentrated brightness renders them conspicuous at great distances. They do not "melt into the landscape" as do the distant galactic clusters.

The distribution in galactic longitude of the globular clusters is most striking and shouts to all who will hear of the eccentric position of the sun. All but a few of them are in one half of the sky and one-third of all known globular clusters are found in a region of Sagittarius that covers only 2 percent of the sky (Fig. 53). The globular clusters form a vast system of their own, concentric with the Milky Way system, but spherical in outline.

Until Shapley's classical investigations of 1916–1919 no measures of the distances of globular clusters were available. His studies of the RR Lyrae variables discovered by Bailey and others led to the first accurate distance estimates for these far-away objects. With the aid of the 60-inch and 100-inch reflectors of Mount Wilson

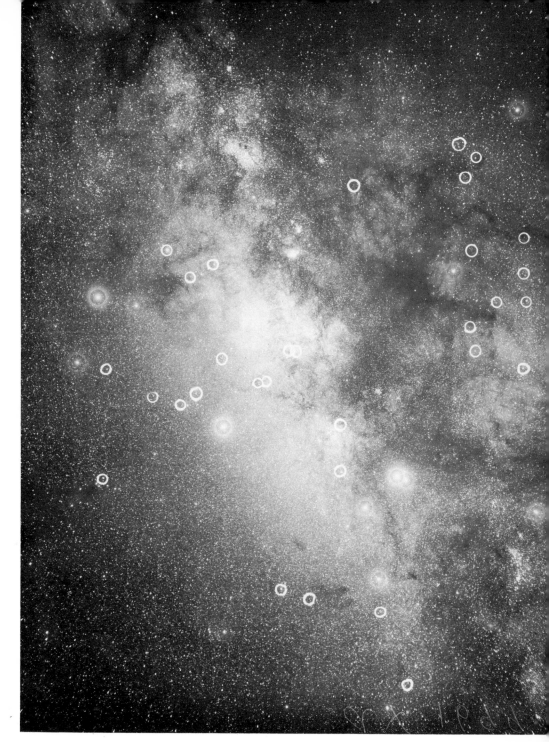

Fig. 53. The direction of the galactic center. The circles mark the positions of globular clusters for this section of the Milky Way. One-third of all known globular clusters are in this photograph, within an area of only 2 percent of the sky. (Harvard Observatory photograph.)

Observatory, Shapley photographed great numbers of the variables frequently enough to obtain accurate light curves, and consequently the distances of all globular clusters with known cluster variables were found.

For those clusters that lacked variables, estimates of the distances were found from the magnitudes of the brightest stars. Shapley noticed that the brightest stars in the globular clusters—unlike the stars in the sun's neighborhood—are not blue-white giants, but are red giants of absolute magnitude about -3, much brighter than the typical red giants found near the sun.

Still other estimates of distance for more distant clusters were based on apparent diameters and apparent integrated magnitudes. Here we are advancing on shaky ground by assuming that globular clusters are all uniform objects and that all apparent differences are due to one variable—the distance from us.

At present cluster-type variables have been identified in about one-third of the clusters. Mrs. Hogg has listed 1100 known variables. For 20 more clusters rough distances have been found from the brightest stars.

To find the distance from our sun to a given globular cluster, we must know not only the apparent magnitude of the RR Lyrae variables in the cluster, but also the amount of intervening space absorption between our sun and the cluster. This is determined from the amount of space reddening. Mayall has found the integrated spectral types for a number of globular clusters; they vary between A5 and G5, with most of them between F8 and G5. Because of this narrow range of integrated spectrum, the true color index of a globular cluster can be predicted fairly well, and from the difference between it and the observed color index the amount of space reddening between the sun and the cluster may be found. By multiplication by a suitable factor the total amount of intervening absorption is obtained and the distance can be corrected for absorption effects. Stebbins and Whitford have measured the color indices for 68 globular clusters. The derived total absolute magnitudes for the globular clusters with known RR Lyrae variables range from $M = -5$ to -8, which is too wide a range to give much confidence in the distances derived from integrated apparent magnitudes alone.

The known system of globular star clusters in our own galaxy is roughly a spherical one, with its center located at a distance of 27,000 light-years from the sun in the direction of galactic longitude

$l = 328°$ (Sagittarius), $b = 0°$ or perhaps $-2°$. We have every reason to suppose that it is concentric with our own galactic system of stars, dust, and nebulae.

*   *

*

Population
Characteristics
of Globular
Clusters

Shapley first pointed out that the kinds of stars found in globular clusters differ in several respects from those in the sun's neighborhood. The brightest stars are red and they are some three magnitudes brighter than the brightest blue-white stars present. He was unable to observe stars fainter than about absolute magnitude $+1$, considerably brighter than stars like our sun.

With the advent of the 200-inch Hale telescope at Mount Palomar it has become possible to make more extensive studies of the nearest globular clusters as to color and magnitude. Thorough studies have been made of Messier 92 by Arp, Baum, and Sandage, of Messier 3 by Sandage, and of Messier 13 by Baum.

In all these cases a magnitude sequence was set up photoelectrically. In the case of Messier 13 the faintest stars were measured by a photo-counting device. Some of these stars—those of the twenty-third magnitude—were so faint that they could not be seen visually through the eyepiece, though their positions were measured on a photographic plate. They were detected by setting for difference in position against a brighter star. For the faintest star it was necessary to observe for 4 hours, and the star's magnitude was derived from the small percentage increase in light over the sky background.

After the basic magnitude sequence was established photoelectrically, stars were interpolated by photographic means. Some 1100 stars were measured in both Messier 3 and Messier 92. Colors were determined by using blue and yellow filters with the photoelectric photometer and blue- and yellow-sensitive plates with suitable filters for the photographic work.

Assuming the RR Lyrae stars to be of zero absolute magnitude, the distance moduli of these clusters are between 14 and 15 magnitudes. This means that the difference $m - M$ amounts to $+14$ or $+15$, so that a star with $m = 20$ will have an absolute magnitude of $+6$ or $+5$, not unlike our sun; observations to the twentieth magnitude or fainter give a good segment of the main sequence to the limit of stars of the same luminosity as our sun. Figure 54 shows the superposition of the three color-magnitude arrays for various globular clusters on the assumption that the RR Lyrae stars are identical in color and magnitude in all globular clusters. Distinct differences are apparent from one cluster to another in the slope of the giant branch, in the number of stars to the left of the variable-star region, and in the color and absolute magnitude of the main sequence. Other superpositions of the three diagrams seem on the whole to present more difficulties than does the one shown here.

It is apparent that, while the clusters differ somewhat from each other, there is a much more striking difference from the Russell-Hertzsprung diagram for the stars in the neighborhood of the sun. We are evidently dealing with two very different populations.

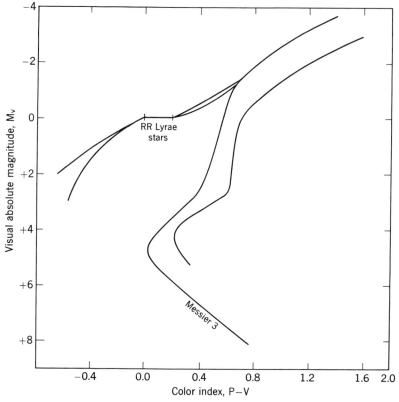

Fig. 54.   Color-luminosity curves for globular clusters. The schematic diagrams shown here are based on observational data assembled at Mount Wilson and Palomar Observatories. The vertical coördinate is the visual absolute magnitude and the $P - V$ (photographic minus visual) color indices are shown horizontally. Note the special place of the RR Lyrae stars and the very faint extension for Messier 3 (Sandage). (Courtesy of *Astrophysical Journal*.)

The feature that at first is most startling is the nearly vertical branch from the giant to the subgiant branches, with nearly constant color for a range of 4 magnitudes in absolute magnitude. There are no stars brighter than +3.5 along the main sequence. Below this point the three main-sequence lines run parallel to the Population I main sequence but at varying distances below and to the left. The main sequence appears to be a broad band rather than a narrow progression.

The number of RR Lyrae stars in the seven globular clusters examined for variables (Messier 10, 13, 92, 2, 15, 5, 3) range from zero in Messier 10 to 165 in Messier 3, and when arranged in this order the other features of the globular clusters seem to follow a general progression in the slope of the giant branch and in the number of stars to the left of the variable-star region. The RR Lyrae stars without exception fall within a narrow range of color and absolute magnitude and there are no nonvariable stars found in this gap. Schwarzschild has suggested that stars of this particular range of temperature and luminosity must be unstable and pulsate and hence become variable stars.

The fact that there are few stars brighter than $M = +3.5$ on the main sequence can possibly be explained as an evolutionary process. In a globular cluster in all likelihood no new stars are being formed at present, since the basic building blocks of star formation—interstellar gas and dust—are not observed in any globular cluster. The stars in a cluster are all presumably of the same age and the absence of stars above a certain point along the main sequence can be used to determine the age of the cluster. According to the Schönberg-Chandrasekhar theory for stars in which mixing within the central core does not occur, luminous stars should move to the right as they leave the main sequence. For Messier 91 and Messier 3 the time since all stars were on the main sequence has been estimated as 5×10^9 years; the O and B stars should have burned themselves out long ago, even if they had once existed.

Early studies of the luminosity functions in globular clusters were made by Shapley about 40 years ago. The subject remained rather neglected until, quite recently, Sandage made a study of the luminosity function of M 3. Since his photographic plates reach to apparent magnitude 22.5 and since the distance modulus of the cluster is 15.6, he observes stars with absolute magnitudes from −3 to +7. From plates of different exposure times, he counted the number of stars of different magnitudes within 8 minutes of arc from the center. Sandage's luminosity function for Messier 3, based on 44,000 stars, is given in Fig. 55, where it is compared with the luminosity function of van Rhijn for the neighborhood of the sun.

The hump at zero magnitude is very evident. It includes some 200 cluster-type variables and other stars with color indices to the blue of $+0.4$. The drop after $M = +5.5$ Sandage feels is undoubtedly real, though the slope of the curve beyond that point is of course uncertain.

From the number of stars of each absolute magnitude it is possible to compute the contribution of stars of each magnitude to the total light. The value from the summation of the contributions is $M = -8.09$, which is in good agreement with the integrated absolute magnitude of -8.42 found by Christie. Ninety percent of the light of the cluster comes from stars brighter than the fourth absolute magnitude, that is, brighter than the sun, although the total number of stars like the sun and fainter is very large.

Since it is impossible at present to go below $M = +7$, Sandage uses the van Rhijn luminosity function to estimate the total number of stars of all luminosities in the cluster. This gives the total mass as 1.4×10^5 solar masses. Wilson and Miss Coffeen estimated the total mass of Messier 92 from dynamical theory as 3.3×10^5. In

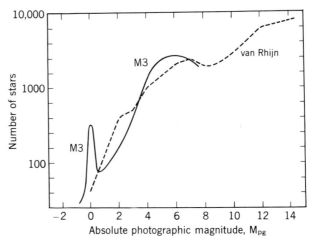

Fig. 55.   The luminosity function for Messier 3. Sandage has counted stars in successive intervals of photographic absolute magnitude in the globular cluster Messier 3. In the diagram his derived luminosity function is compared with that of van Rhijn in Fig. 40, which applies to the vicinity of the sun. (Courtesy of *Astronomical Journal*.)

view of the greater luminosity of Messier 3 as compared with Messier 92, its dynamical mass should come out of the order of 5.6×10^5, larger than the above value by a factor 4. It is still uncertain whether this discrepancy is real. If it is real it would mean that the number of faint dwarf stars is much greater in the globular cluster than in the neighborhood of our sun.

*   *

*

The Nucleus of Our Galaxy

Before the work of Shapley (1916–1919), it had been generally assumed that our sun is not very far from the center of our galaxy, that the stars thin out in all directions away from the sun, and that the diameter of the whole system would hardly exceed 30,000 light-years. To Shapley belongs the credit of having shown that we are nowhere near the center and that the nucleus of our galaxy lies at a great distance, now estimated at 27,000 light-years, from the sun in the direction of Sagittarius. The best modern values for the direction of the center place it at galactic longitude $l = 328°$, latitude $b = 0°$, or perhaps $-2°$.

The over-all picture of the surface distribution of faint stars over the sky directly supports the hypothesis that the star clouds in Sagittarius mark the direction toward the center of our galaxy. On Schmidt photographs that reach to faint limits the stars along the Milky Way are most dense in the Sagittarius section. If one looks back upon the history of Milky Way research, it does seem surprising that it took until 1916–1919 (Shapley's researches) before astronomers began to realize that we are far from the center of the galaxy and that the Sagittarius cloud marks the direction to the center. The evidence was there all along, but no one took an unprejudiced look at the sky!

The most direct evidence has come from the studies of the distribution of RR Lyrae stars outside globular clusters. Their distribution resembles rather closely that of the globular clusters themselves. Many are found at great distances from the central plane of our galaxy and they occur in great numbers in the general direction of Scorpius and Sagittarius. One must be very careful in selecting fields for further searches and study of RR Lyrae variables, since one obviously will not gain much by dealing with parts of the sky for which relatively strong nearby overlying obscuration is present. The researches of the future are to be limited to unobscured or very lightly obscured fields where our observations can reach to great distances.

With the 100-inch Hooker reflector of Mount Wilson Observatory, Baade photographed a region at $l = 328°$, $b = -4.3°$, which is remarkably free from local obscuration. Observed color indices and derived color excesses for two globular clusters in the field show that the total photographic absorption for that direction is less than 3 magnitudes for the entire stretch between our sun and the center. Baade's plates reach to $m = 20$ and they show conclusively, first, that there are very great numbers of RR Lyrae variables among the faint stars and, second, that there is a definite maximum to the

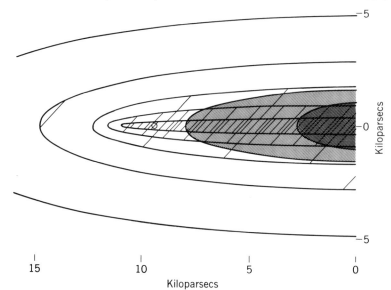

Fig. 56.   A schematic model of the galactic system by Oort. The diagram shows a section perpendicular to the galactic plane, through the center and the sun. The position of the sun is indicated by a small circle. The large central ellipsoid has axes of lengths 8 and 1.61 kiloparsecs and a density of 2.15 (using the density near the sun as a unit); the small central ellipsoid, with axes of lengths 2.8 and 1 kiloparsecs, has a density of 3.13. (The reader is reminded that 1 kiloparsec = 3258 light-years.) The lengths of the axes (kiloparsecs) and the densities of the five outer ellipsoids are as follows:

axes 11.0,	0.3	density 0.446
11.6,	.9	.104
12.3,	1.7	.026
14.8,	2.8	.007
20.3,	4.9	.003

The ellipsoids are superimposed upon one another. (Courtesy of *Astrophysical Journal*.)

numbers of these variables at $m = 17.5$, at an apparent magnitude well above the plate limit $m = 20$. Baade and S. Gaposchkin—who assisted in the measurement and analysis of the variables—estimate from their data that the center of our galaxy is at a distance of the order of 27,000 light-years from our sun.

Other stars show this marked concentration to the center of our galaxy. Long-period and irregular variable stars and especially the new stars, or novae, occur in the Sagittarius-Scorpius section of the Milky Way in greater abundance than almost anywhere else. Infrared surveys by Nassau, van Albada, and Blanco at the Warner and Swasey Observatory and by Haro at the observatory in Tonanzintla, Mexico, have revealed that the late M-type giant stars (M5 and later) show little tendency toward clustering, but instead increase in numbers uniformly toward the galactic center. The results of a recent Southern Hemisphere survey by Henry and Elske Smith at the Boyden Station confirm this phenomenon when one approaches the center from the southernmost parts of the band of the Milky Way. One type of object that is of interest in this connection is the planetary nebulae. These are gaseous shells or disks of relatively small dimensions, often centered upon a hot star that may have been a nova or supernova in the past. Minkowski's researches on the distribution of planetary nebulae have revealed that the fainter planetaries show a great preference for the Sagittarius-Scorpius section. Unusual abundance for the central region of our galaxy is a definite characteristic of Population II stars.

It should be stated clearly that the brilliant Great Cloud in Sagittarius is, probably only an edge of a very extended nuclear region. Most of the larger nucleus of our galaxy is hidden from view by overlying obscurations. Bok and van Wijk have demonstrated that this obscuration originates close to the sun (at distances of the order of one-tenth and less of the distance to the center). In most places this local fog is so dense that only radio waves can penetrate it, but in a few not too dense places infrared-sensitive emulsions show what lies on the other side of the fog. Dufay in France and Henry Smith at the Boyden Station have taken photographs in infrared light that show some globular clusters not detected previously by photographs in normal blue light. Some of these same dark regions can be penetrated by photoelectric techniques adapted to the infrared. The broad outlines of the nuclear region have been shown as a result of special studies by Stebbins and Whitford in the United

States and by Nikonov and Holopov in the Soviet Union. The nuclear region appears to measure 5000 light-years or more across.

Another approach to the problem of the study of the properties of the central region of our galaxy is to investigate the influence that the galactic nucleus will have on the stellar distribution at great distance from the central plane. There are various lines of evidence —from star counts, from studies of the distribution of RR Lyrae variables and from radio data—that suggest the presence of a thin but very extended halo or corona of our galaxy. From studies of this halo it has been possible to derive models for the mass distribution in our galaxy. A model of this sort by Oort and his associates at Leiden is given in Fig. 56. It shows clearly the thin outer ellipsoids of the halo and also the very dense inner ellipsoids of the galactic nucleus.

5

The Whirling Galaxy

Thus far we have dealt only with the purely structural aspects of the Milky Way problem. Now we shall turn to considerations involving the motions of the stars and the forces that control them; we shall see what may be learned about the *dynamics* of the system from studies of the regularities in the proper motions and radial velocities of the stars and clusters of stars.

We found the Milky Way system to be a highly flattened one, embedded in a very tenuous, more nearly spherical halo. The characteristic spiral arms, outlined by the O and B stars and by bright and dark nebulae, lie in or very near the central plane of the galaxy. The sun is probably about 27,000 light-years distant from the dense central nucleus, but it is within 100 light-years of the central plane.

It should have been evident all along that the flattened shape of our galaxy is indicative of rapid symmetrical rotation about an axis perpendicular to the plane, but it was not until 1926–27 that the researches of Lindblad and Oort first gave conclusive proof of this *galactic rotation*. In the first section of the present chapter we shall present the evidence to show that our sun and the great majority of the stars in our vicinity move about the galactic center in roughly circular orbits and with speeds of somewhat more than 200 kilometers per second. Most of the regularities observed in the motions of the stars near the sun and those at distances up to a few thousand light-years can be understood on the basis of galactic rotation.

* *

*

The Sun's Motion Around the Galactic Center

The highly flattened shape of the system of O and B stars and even of the system of stars like our sun suggests that these subsystems of our galaxy are in rapid rotation. The situation is quite different for the globular clusters, which form a tenuous, almost spherical, subsystem, surrounding the flattened principal Milky Way system. Inside such a system of spherical shape there may be large random motions, but rotation as a whole is hardly likely. On the average, the globular clusters should define a system more or less at rest with respect to the center of our galaxy. From the study of the observed radial velocities of globular clusters, we should be able to obtain information about the sun's motion relative to them and hence presumably with reference to the center of our galaxy.

Observed radial velocities are available for 50 globular clusters. The majority of these radial velocities were measured by Mayall at the Lick Observatory, who found individual values ranging between $+291$ and -360 kilometers per second. The spectral lines are often broad and fuzzy, and precise measurement is far from simple (Fig. 57). To make matters worse, the distribution of the globular clusters over the sky is so uneven as to make difficult the evaluation of the position of the apex of the sun's motion and its speed. In spite of these obstacles, Mayall has been able to derive a value of the sun's motion relative to the system of the globular clusters of 200 kilometers per second directed toward a point in the galactic plane at galactic longitude $l = 55°$, which is just about 90° from the direction to the center of our galaxy; he estimates that the derived solar speed is uncertain by 25 kilometers per second. Mayall has cautioned astronomers against the use of the value of 200 kilometers per sec-

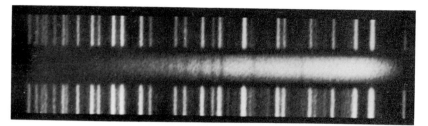

Fig. 57.   Spectrum of globular cluster NGC 6341. (Lick Observatory photograph by Mayall.)

ond for the rotational velocity of our sun relative to the galactic center, since he considers it likely that the system of the globular clusters—which shows some slight degree of flattening—may have a residual rotation of 50 kilometers per second or more.

Evidence pointing to a value of the circular velocity of the sun and its neighbors greater than 200 kilometers per second has come principally from radial-velocity data for neighboring galaxies determined at the Mount Wilson and Palomar and the Lick Observatories. Together with the Large and Small Magellanic Clouds, the spiral galaxies in Andromeda and Triangulum, and half a dozen smaller objects, our galaxy forms a sort of local supersystem. If we assume a motion of the order of 250 to 270 kilometers per second toward galactic longitude $l = 55°$ for our sun relative to the center of our galaxy, then we find that the relative speeds of all galaxies of the group become small.

The above evidence alone seems to point to a speed of at least 250 kilometers per second for our sun and its neighbors relative to the center of our galaxy. But there is other evidence, from radio studies of the velocities in the central regions of our galaxy and from related dynamical considerations of the forces that control the motions and distributions of the stars in the core of our galaxy, that supports quite strongly a lower value—of the order of 220 kilometers per second. Since the center of our galaxy may well have a speed of 30 to 50 kilometers per second relative to the average for our neighbor galaxies, we shall assume, for the time being, that 220 kilometers per second toward galactic longitude $l = 55°$ represents the most likely value of the sun's motion relative to the center of our galaxy. No one has questioned the assertion that our sun moves in a very nearly circular orbit around the center of our Milky Way system.

*   *

*

The Stars of High Velocity   Most of the stars near the sun move with speeds relative to the sun not in excess of 30 kilometers per second, but there are some that exceed this limit by a wide margin. We are accustomed to refer to the stars with velocities in excess of 60 kilometers per second relative to the sun as *stars of high velocity;* Miss Roman has published a catalogue with 600 such stars. In Fig. 58 we have reproduced a diagram in which the velocity arrows for the high-velocity stars within 65 light-years of the sun are shown projected on the plane of the Milky Way system. With practically no exception, the stars are seen to move toward the half of the Milky Way between galactic longitudes $l = 150°$ and $l = 330°$ (from Auriga, through Orion, to Carina and Sagittarius-Scorpio). Not a single high-velocity star shows a motion directed toward the Cygnus section of the Milky

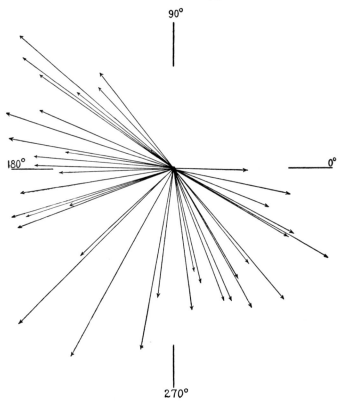

Fig. 58.   The asymmetry in stellar motions. The diagram gives the distribution in the galactic plane of the directions of the velocities of nearby stars with speeds in excess of 60 km/sec. The galactic longitudes of these directions are indicated. Not a single star in the diagram is found to move in a direction between galactic longitudes $l = 350°$ and $l = 120°$; the center of the sector of avoidance is at $l = 55°$.

Way ($l = 55°$). If we determine the average motion of the stars shown in Fig. 58 relative to our sun we find it directed toward galactic longitude $l = 235°$; from this we deduce that the sun moves relative to these stars in the direction exactly opposite, $l = 55°$. The apex of the sun's motion relative to the high-velocity stars thus agrees with that derived from the radial velocities of the globular clusters.

The RR Lyrae variables are the most striking group of high-velocity stars; they give a value for the sun's apex at $l = 50°$, with an average speed relative to the sun of 130 kilometers per second. These stars are arranged in a subsystem that is not quite spherical but has some slight flattening; they are highly concentrated toward the nucleus of our galaxy. The observed flattening of the system of the RR Lyrae stars suggests some residual rotation of the system as a whole, though considerably less than for our sun; the observed degree of flattening is consistent with a rotational speed of 130 kilometers per second for the RR Lyrae stars as a whole relative to the center of our galaxy. The purely random motions of the RR Lyrae stars (found after correction for systematic motions) come out quite high—of the order of 100 kilometers per second.

The amazing motion characteristics of the high-velocity stars were first studied thoroughly by Oort and by Strömberg in 1924. One of the most extensive surveys of this variety of stars was published in 1940 by Miczaika, who, at that time, was able to list 555 stars with velocities in excess of 63 kilometers per second. Certain varieties of stars contain a much higher percentage of high-velocity stars. Practically none occur among the B stars, whereas they occur rather frequently among the M stars, where we find 19 percent of high-velocity stars among the stars fainter than $m = 7.25$.

Lindblad, who was the originator of the theory of galactic rotation, developed the theory especially to explain the observed asymmetry in the motions of the high-velocity stars. He thought of the Milky Way system as made up of a number of concentric subsystems, each with its own peculiar degree of flattening and rotational speed relative to the galactic center. Even today this approach retains considerable validity and is being used extensively in the work of the Soviet astronomers Kukarkin and Parenago. According to this concept, the sun and all the stars with observed low velocities (less than 20 or 30 kilometers per second) relative to the sun whiz around the galactic center at a rate of about 220 kilometers per second. The RR Lyrae variables, with an average speed of 130 kilometers per second relative to the sun directed opposite to where the sun is heading, are really the laggards and their average rotational speed is no more than $220 - 120 = 100$ kilometers per second relative to the center of the galaxy (Fig. 59).

But, you might ask, why are there not also some stars of really

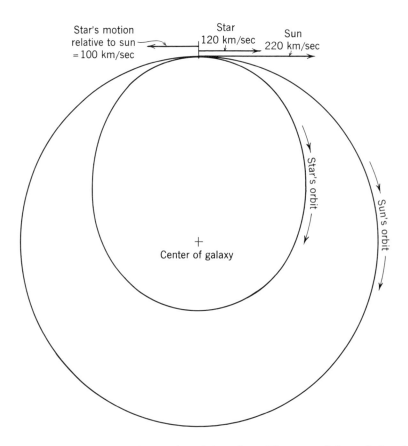

Fig. 59.   Asymmetry and the rotation of the galaxy. The sun and the majority of the stars near us move around the center of our galaxy in roughly circular orbits with velocities of the order of 220 km/sec. A star that would move in an elongated galactic orbit such as is shown here might have a velocity of only 120 km/sec at the point where the orbit reaches as far as the sun. This star would be observed from the sun and earth as having a "high" velocity of 100 km/sec directed opposite to that of the general galactic rotation. If it were observed to have a velocity with respect to the sun and its neighbors as high as 100 km/sec in the direction of galactic rotation, then its speed relative to the galactic center would be 320 km/sec and the star would in all likelihood not be a permanent member of our galactic system.

high velocity moving with speeds of 90 kilometers per second relative to the sun in the direction of galactic longitude $l = 55°$? Such stars would have velocities relative to the center of our galaxy of the order of 310 kilometers per second and our galaxy apparently does not retain such speeders. A velocity in excess of 300 kilometers per second relative to the galactic center is apparently sufficiently great to permit the star to escape freely from our galaxy.

*   *

*

Solar Motion and Star Streaming

We return now briefly to a consideration of the motions of the normal stars of all spectral classes and luminosities that are relatively near to the sun. We saw in Chapter 3 that the sun moves with a speed of 18 or 20 kilometers per second toward a solar apex in the constellation Hercules when the motion is referred to the average of the nearby stars as a standard of rest.

The motion of the sun is not found to have the same value for all classes of stars. As early as 1910 Campbell at the Lick Observatory suggested that the derived solar motion varies with spectral class. He found that the B stars give a rather small solar motion and that the value increases as we proceed from spectral class A through F to G and K but becomes somewhat more like the B average for the M stars. Later work has shown that there is a marked dependence of the value of the solar motion upon the intrinsic luminosities of the stars, with the M dwarfs giving, for instance, a much larger solar motion than the M giants.

The researches of the Vyssotskys of the University of Virginia show that both the position of the apex and the value of the solar motion depend rather markedly on the spectral class and average apparent magnitude of the stars with respect to which the motion is determined. The position of the apex for the A and F stars is found at lower galactic latitude than for the other types. The differences in position of the apex and value of the sun's speed are probably due in part to effects of moving clusters, and for the rest they are caused by an uneven admixture of high-velocity stars and by local differences from pure circular galactic rotation.

We turn now to the subject of *star streaming*. Throughout the nineteenth century, astronomers were blissfully unaware of any regularities in stellar motions beyond those arising from the reflex of the sun's motion. Then, in 1904, Kapteyn of Holland announced the discovery of the two star streams. With this discovery came the first realization that the stars are not moving in a perfectly haphazard fashion, but that their motions are subject to general laws.

Kapteyn's researches dealt with the proper motions of the brighter stars in the sky. The celestial sphere was marked off into a number of sections, in each of which Kapteyn counted the number of stars moving within certain narrow limits of direction. A plot of the proper motions on a chart or on a celestial sphere showed directly how many were moving within 15° of the direction of the North Pole in the sky, how many within 15° of the northwest direction, and so on.

A diagram such as Fig. 60 summarizes the observed distribution of directions in a convenient fashion. We draw for each particular direction an arrow, the length of which is proportional to the number of stars found traveling in that direction. By connecting the

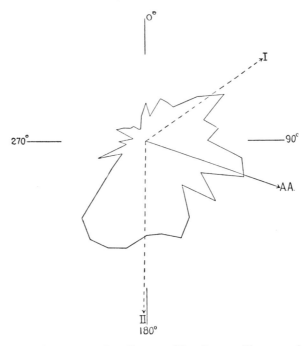

Fig. 60.   A typical star-streaming diagram. The diagram illustrates the distribution of the directions of proper motions, measured by Smart, for a small region of the sky; the arrow *AA* marks the direction toward the antapex. The broken arrows I and II show the directions of the two star streams for this section of the sky.

ends of these arrows by straight lines we obtain a clear representation of the distribution of the directions of proper motions for each section of the sky.

If the stars were moving perfectly at random, and if the sun had no motion of its own, the lines connecting the points in the diagram would form a circle. The sun's motion would have the effect of drawing this circle out into an elongated figure resembling an ellipse, the long axis of which should point away from the apex of the sun's motion. For fields not far from the apex and antapex the figure should be almost circular and the greatest flattening should be found along the circle on the sphere halfway between the apex and antapex.

To make a long story short, we find nothing of the kind. The curves near the apex and antapex are by no means circular, and simple figures shaped like ellipses are not observed. The characteristic feature is that the figures are bilobed. Generally two directions are found which the stars in a given section seem to prefer.

It was soon seen that these streaming effects are not purely local. For each section we can draw the two preferred directions and if we plot these on a celestial sphere they all appear to point very closely to two points on the sphere. The points were called by Kapteyn the *apparent vertices* of his two star streams. If the observed streaming tendencies were of a random character, we would have found no regularity in the distribution of these arrows over the sphere. The fact that each stream shows a well-marked convergent point is excellent proof that the stars all over the sky show in their motions preference for either Stream I or Stream II.

The Kapteyn star streaming bears some resemblance to the convergent effect observed for the stars of a moving cluster such as the Hyades cluster. In the case of the moving cluster the proper motion vectors of all individual members were found to pass exactly through the convergent. The motions of the stars that belong to one of Kapteyn's streams show only a tendency to move along with the general stream motion rather than at right angles to it. They still insist on preserving their right to deviate considerably from the path of streaming instead of submitting to the Hyades-like regimentation.

It is not difficult to correct for the effect of the sun's motion and derive the position of the vertices as viewed from a star supposed to be at rest with respect to the average of all its neighbors. Kapteyn showed that the *true vertices* of star streaming, found after correcting for solar motion, fall at opposite points in the sky, one in Scutum, the other in Orion.

It was not surprising that the true vertices are 180° apart in the sky, because, by correcting for local solar motion, we have automatically balanced the motions in the streams. But it was surprising, and highly significant, that the line of the true vertices falls exactly in the Milky Way, and we note in passing that one vertex lies in the sky not far from the direction of the galactic center. Since the two vertices are 180° apart in the sky, the line joining them will pass nearly through the galactic center. An explanation was not directly forthcoming, but at the time of Kapteyn's discovery it was realized that this represented some major clue for the ultimate solution of the riddle of the Milky Way.

Subsequent researches by Eddington and Karl Schwarzschild and more recent studies by many astronomers, most notably by the Vyssotskys at the McCormick Observatory, have confirmed and extended Kapteyn's work. Schwarzschild showed that it was unnecessary to think in terms of two specific streams of stars. He pointed out that the line of the true vertices marks the direction along which the stars prefer to move. He found methods for expressing the spread, or *dispersion,* of the motions along the direction of the true vertices and for two mutually perpendicular directions at right angles to the line of the true vertices. This dispersion is always greatest along the line of the true vertices; it is slightly less (0.6 to 0.7 of the first quantity) for the direction at right angles to this line in the galactic plane, and still somewhat smaller for the direction at right angles to the galactic plane.

Lindblad was the first astronomer to prove that star streaming according to the picture of Schwarzschild is a natural consequence of the rotation of our galaxy. The majority of stars move in orbits that are almost, but not quite, circular around the center of our galaxy. These slightly oval orbits in the galactic plane—or slightly inclined with respect to the plane—produce observable deviations from pure circular motion and Lindblad could show that, on the average, the stars would have a slightly greater spread in their motions toward or away from the center than at right angles to this direction.

According to the purest form of the theory of our rotating galaxy, the line of the true vertices should pass precisely through the galactic center. This happy state of affairs is not observed, for the vertex for some groups of stars lies as much as 15° away from the direction to the center. The explanation of this observed deviation is probably found in the nonuniform distribution of the stars near the galactic plane. We have spiral arms in our galaxy and variable stellar density between the spiral arms. In the arms themselves there are concentrations of many sorts, from extended star clouds and aggregates to expanding associations. We live in a part of our galaxy that is far removed from the well-mixed state envisioned by the simplest form of the theory of a rotating galaxy. Vertex deviation may well provide in the future the clue to the intricate relations that must exist between local variations in stellar distribution and local velocity characteristics.

*   *

*

Galactic Rotation

After Lindblad had presented his explanation of the observed asymmetry in stellar motions, Oort found a further proof for the general rotation of our galaxy in the radial velocities and proper motions of the stars between 1000 and 10,000 light-years from the sun. Oort reasoned that it is very unlikely that our galaxy should rotate like a solid wheel. If it did, the stars would keep their same relative positions and there would be no evidence of motion except from the galaxies. If a considerable part of the total mass of our galaxy is concentrated near the galactic nucleus, we should rather expect that the motions of the stars in our galaxy would resemble those of the planets around the sun. Venus moves faster than the earth and

TABLE 4. CIRCULAR VELOCITY OF GALACTIC ROTATION AT VARIOUS DISTANCES FROM THE GALACTIC CENTER.

Distance (lt-yr)	Velocity (km/sec)
0	0
5,000	150*
10,000	190*
15,000	220*
20,000	230
25,000†	224
30,000	213
35,000	197
40,000	180

* These values are very uncertain.
† The sun's distance is 27,000 light-years.

the earth in turn outruns Mars, and in the same fashion the stars nearer the galactic center could be expected to complete a galactic circuit in shorter time than those farther from the center. We might offhand doubt that this conclusion would hold for our galaxy, since (see Table 4) the circular velocity of rotation around the galactic center does not vary in the manner of the planets of our solar system. Table 4 does show, however, that the stars closest to the galactic center complete a circuit more quickly than the more distant ones. Take, for example, the value of the circular velocity of 190 kilometers per second listed in Table 4 for an object at 10,000 light-years from the galactic center. If our galaxy were rotating like a solid wheel, the corresponding circular velocity at 20,000 light-years would have to be twice as large, 380 kilometers per second. Instead, Table 4 lists a value of 230 kilometers per second at a distance of 20,000 light-years, thus suggesting that the more distant parts of our galaxy lag behind relative to the nearer ones in the completion of one full revolution around the galactic center.

Since all our observations are made from the earth, which accompanies our sun, we ask what observable effects in the radial velocities there might be for an observer on the sun. Oort showed that, as viewed from the sun, some distant stars would seem to be catching up with us, others would seem to be receding. He found that the effect in the radial velocities would go through its range of values twice as we observe completely around the galactic circle. Figure 61 shows how this comes about.

In the diagram on the left the arrows indicate how the velocity of rotation decreases with increasing distance from the galactic center. In the second diagram, showing the region around the sun, the effect of the solar motion has been removed and the arrows represent the velocities as seen from the sun. They show the effects of the differential galactic rotation. The components of these velocities along the radii passing through the sun will be the effects of differential galactic rotation on radial velocities.

At four points along the circle there should be no approach or recession of the stars due to galactic rotation, and the observed effect in the radial velocities is there zero. These are the directions toward and away from the galactic center and at right angles to that line. Halfway between these points one diagonal line shows the direction in which the stars will on the average be receding and hence show positive radial velocities, and along the other diagonal

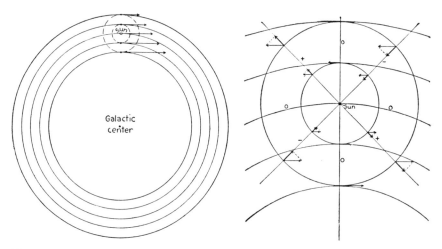

Fig. 61.   The effects of galactic rotation on radial velocities. The diagram on the left illustrates a possible variation of rotational velocity with distance from the galactic center. In the diagram on the right we reproduce on a larger scale the region around the sun. The arrows now represent the velocities as observed from the sun. The radial components of these velocities are shown and these exhibit the variation of galactic rotation with galactic longitude, as described in the text.

they should show on the average negative radial velocities corresponding to approach. The result will be, as we plot the average observed radial velocities against the galactic longitude, a curve with a double wave, going through two maxima and two minima for the complete circle of longitudes. It is important to note that the galactic rotation effect in the radial velocities will be largest for the most distant stars. Oort showed that for distances up to 10,000 light-years from our sun the effect should increase very nearly proportionally to the distance from the sun.

It may be of interest to reproduce the simple mathematical expression for the galactic rotation effect in radial velocities in the form first given by Oort. If V is the effect in the radial velocity, r the average distance of the stars under consideration, l the galactic longitude of the star, and l_o the longitude of the galactic center, we have

$$V = rA \sin 2(l-l_o),$$

a formula that may be readily checked against Fig. 61. The factor A in the formula is generally known as "Oort's constant" and it measures the maximum effect V at the standard distance. The most commonly accepted value of Oort's constant is about 5 to 6 kilometers per second per 1000 light-years. Weaver of the University of

California has presented arguments that suggest 4 kilometers per second per 1000 light-years as a more likely value. Most workers in the field seem agreed that $l_0 = 328°$ or very close to that value.

The stars that have proved most useful in studies of the galactic-rotation effect are distant, intrinsically luminous objects like O and B stars, galactic clusters, and long-period Cepheids. The last have proved of somewhat dubious usefulness because of the uncertainties regarding the absolute magnitudes to be assigned for classical Cepheids with periods of several days or more.

In the past few years a new approach to the study of galactic rotation through radial velocities has become possible. Because of the new system of spectral-absolute-magnitude classification and our present ability to measure precisely color indices and color excesses, we may now determine fairly accurate individual distances for all O and B stars observed for radial velocities. We correct the observed radial velocity first for the effect of reflex of the standard solar motion of 20 kilometers per second toward Hercules. After this has been done, we may assume that the principal radial velocity that remains represents the projection in the line of sight of the difference in circular motion of galactic rotation at the star and at the sun. If we assume for the circular velocity of rotation of the sun the value of 220 kilometers per second quoted early in this chapter, then we find directly the value of the circular velocity at the star's distance from the center of our galaxy. The method that we are describing had its origin in work by Camm in the 1930's, but its application has become possible only in recent years, with the advent of modern techniques of spectral-absolute-magnitude classification.

The values given in Table 4 represent the best that we can probably do to date. No direct observations are available for distances less than 20,000 light-years from the galactic center. We observe no stars directly in this range and our only method for gathering data is with the aid of the radio radiation from neutral hydrogen. The data are still very uncertain, but the velocities given in Table 4 are the best we have. The correction and completion of this table is one of the big future tasks of Milky Way research.

Oort's theory of galactic rotation predicts also an effect in the proper motions of the stars. The effect in these transverse motions reaches its extreme values where the radial velocity effect is zero. We measure our proper motions, however, in seconds of arc per year and not in kilometers per second. If we go twice as far out the linear effect will be doubled but in the observed angular motions the effect will remain unchanged. The effect in the proper motions should therefore vary only with the galactic longitude of the stars involved and not with their distances.

Unfortunately, it is far more difficult to detect the galactic-rotation effect in the proper motions than in the radial velocities. But work by Hins and Blaauw at the Leiden Observatory and also by the Vyssotskys at the McCormick Observatory confirm the generally assumed values of the longitude of the center and of Oort's constants. Weaver at the University of California does not agree with these rather optimistic conclusions and he has expressed the view that proper-motion data require careful further examination before dependable results may be expected from them.

Before we leave the subject of galactic rotation, we should inquire briefly into the shapes of the orbits in which some of the varieties of stars move in our galaxy. The sun's motion differs only slightly from the circular galactic rotation in its neighborhood. We can think of the sun as moving in an ellipse of small eccentricity, while at the same time it vibrates slowly perpendicularly to the galactic plane. It will probably stay at all times within 500 light-years of the galactic plane, and it should complete between two and three oscillations in the perpendicular direction in the 200,000,000 years that it takes to complete one revolution around the galaxy.

The sun and the majority of the Population I stars have motions that differ by not more than 20 kilometers per second from pure circular motion, that is, by less than 10 percent. Hence all of their orbits differ only slightly from pure circular orbits and these stars are in all likelihood now at about the same distance from the center of our galaxy at which they found themselves at the time of their birth, 5 billion years or less ago. The O and B stars, Cepheids, galactic clusters, and interstellar gas clouds follow most nearly the circular orbits of pure galactic rotation. Some of these types—notably the O and B stars—are presumably quite young and we shall see later that their probable ages are only a small fraction of one galactic revolution.

The RR Lyrae stars and other fast-moving stars are presumably following elongated orbits shaped somewhat like ellipses. One wonders how close such stars may once have come to our galactic center. Martin Schwarzschild of Princeton has shown that these stars, in spite of their large peculiar motions, have probably never been much nearer the center than half-way to the sun. Miss Roman of the Yerkes Observatory has, however, discovered some weakline F stars with very elongated galactic orbits. Some of them have velocities that differ so much from pure circular motion that they must have come from points within 5000 light-years of the center of our galaxy. They are probably the best-known stellar representatives that have been shot out to our remote galactic outpost, directly from the very heart of our galaxy. By the study of its present motion, we may learn much about the past history of a star.

The theory of galactic rotation is a great advance in our understanding of the observed regularities in stellar motions. It has provided us with very reasonable explanations of star streaming and of high-velocity stars, and has further led to the discovery of the Oort effects. It is now proving extremely useful in interpreting the observations of the 21-centimeter radiation from neutral hydrogen (Chapter 8).

We should, however, bear in mind that Oort's picture of a smoothly rotating galaxy can at best be only a first and very rough approximation to the true state of affairs in our complex galactic system. The presence of spiral arms, of expanding clusters and streams, of irregularities of distribution and motion, all contribute to the intricacies of the problem. At the same time they hold the key to the past and to future developments.

6

The Interstellar Gas

Diffuse Bright Nebulae

Many of our readers have probably viewed the Great Nebula in Orion through a telescope. The soft greenish hue of the nebulous mass, gradually dimming toward the edge of the field, its erratic though immobile shadings, smooth and mellow in spots, hard and sharp elsewhere, together with the diamondlike scintillations of the four closely packed stars of the Trapezium, present a picture of unsurpassed beauty (Fig. 62). No telescope has ever been able to resolve this glowing mass into stars, and spectroscopic evidence shows that it is a truly nebulous cloud of gas, shining in the transmitted glory of its central stars. What causes such nebulae to shine?

The Orion nebula has a bright-line spectrum in which the lines of hydrogen, highly ionized oxygen, and helium predominate. Nebulae like the Orion nebula are not self-luminous. Twenty years ago Hubble showed that a very hot star was located in the immediate vicinity of every diffuse nebula that has a spectrum similar to that of the Orion nebula.

Fig. 62.   The Orion Nebula. (Mount Wilson and Palomar photograph.)

The physical theory that explains why and how such nebulae shine is quite simple. The densities and pressures in the nebulae are so low that according to earthly standards we would consider any one of them a perfect vacuum. In our physical laboratories an atom is never left alone for any length of time; it is constantly bumping into one of its companions or into the walls of the container. If we wish to observe the atomic processes in their majestic simplicity we shall have to turn to the diffuse nebulae, or clouds of interstellar gas, which are apparently the only places where atoms are left alone enough to perform without undue disturbances.

The atoms in the nebular gas are being bombarded in a very leisurely fashion by the radiation from surrounding stars. The only light quanta that can produce any real excitement are those of very high frequency sent out in abundance by the blue-white stars of spectral types B and O. Most quanta of lower frequencies will simply filter through the gas without bothering it, or being bothered, to any appreciable extent. If a quantum of very high frequency strikes a neutral atom it may transfer enough energy to the atom to cause the expulsion of an electron. The atom is then no longer electrically neutral, but positively charged, or ionized. It becomes an ion, and the process is known as photoionization. The electron is free and starts off by itself on a journey through interstellar space. What can happen to the electron? With its negative charge it is ready to combine with any positively charged ion that is available, but it soon discovers that there are very few of these ions. Our positive ion is equally hampered in its search for a free electron that would return it to the neutral state. An atom once ionized may travel for days or months before it encounters a free electron to neutralize its charge. In the interstellar laboratories physical processes operate in unhurried and leisurely ways. An atom inside a star, or in one of the physical laboratories on the earth, is constantly being bumped and jostled. The atoms in the nebulae, however, live alone and like it.

Occasionally one of the free electrons will be captured by a positively charged ion. Let us suppose that a capture is made by a hydrogen ion, that is, a proton. According to modern atomic theory, the neutral hydrogen atom has only a limited number of permitted orbits in which the electron can move about the proton (Fig. 63). Each such orbit has a definite energy for the electron relative to the proton with which it is associated. When an electron is captured

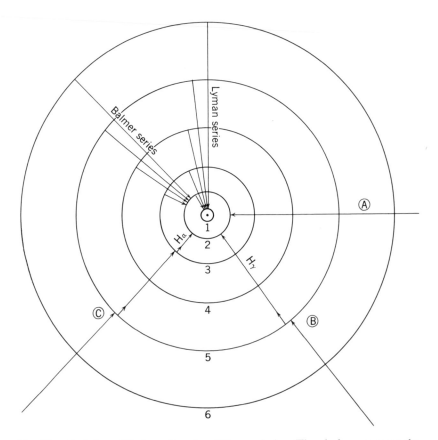

Fig. 63.   Emission of Balmer lines by diffuse nebulae. The circles represent the relative energy levels of the electron in the hydrogen atom, with *1* indicating the lowest or Lyman level, *2* the Balmer level, *3* the Paschen level, and so on. The Balmer series and the Lyman series are shown by arrows representing transitions from higher levels to the Balmer and Lyman levels, respectively. The lines *A, B,* and *C* show ways in which an electron may be captured by a proton to produce a neutral atom in the Balmer level. In *A* the electron is captured immediately in the Balmer level and as a result a quantum in the Balmer continuum is emitted. In *B* and *C* the capture takes place in level 5 with the emission of an infrared quantum in the continuum for level 5. In *B* this capture is followed by a direct transition to the Balmer level and emission of the Hγ line. In *C* the first transition is from level 5 to level 3 and then follows a transition to the Balmer level with the emission of the Hα line. The electron in the hydrogen atom would remain in the Balmer level for 1 one-hundred millionth of a second and then settle down in the lowest or Lyman level.

Fig. 64. The Orion Nebula in infrared light. The photograph shows clearly a marked concentration of very red stars in the region of the gaseous nebula. Comparison with Fig. 62 shows many interesting features. For a comment on the rays and halos, see the legend for Fig. 13. (An enlargement from a hypersensitized infrared plate by Haro made with the Tonanzintla Schmidt telescope.)

by the proton, it can land in any one of the permitted orbits of the neutral hydrogen atom. If the capture takes place in the tightest orbit—that of lowest energy—the whole show will be over at once. A single ultraviolet quantum will then be emitted as a by-product of the capture. Frequently, however, the free electron will be captured in one of the orbits of higher energy. The hydrogen atom cannot remain for more than a small fraction of a second in this excited state and the capture is followed immediately by the collapse of the newly created neutral atom. The electron cascades inward to the orbit of lowest energy, where it will remain until the next ultraviolet quantum comes along to begin another sequence of disruption and ultimate recombination. During the cascading process, the captured electron will go from an orbit of high energy of the neutral hydrogen atom to the lowest energy level. The chances are that somewhere on the way a quantum corresponding to one of the Balmer transitions will be released. The Balmer lines in diffuse nebulae are produced during such internal adjustments in the neutral atom, which follow immediately after the capture of a free electron by a proton.

The beautiful and conspicuous emission nebulae like the Great Nebula in Orion, or the famous nebula near the star Eta Carinae,

Fig. 65.   Objective-prism spectra for a region near the Orion Nebula. The region is that shown in the lower right-hand corner of Figs. 62 and 64 (tilted). A red-sensitive emulsion was used for this photograph by Haro at the Tonanzintla Observatory. The marks (by Haro) indicate stars with the Balmer Hα line in emission.

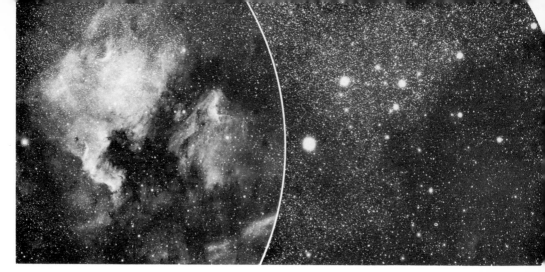

Fig. 66. A matched pair of photographs of the region of the North America Nebula. The left-hand photograph was made on a red-sensitive emulsion and represents the nebula almost entirely in hydrogen Hα light. The right-hand photograph was made on an infrared-sensitive emulsion and with a filter to exclude Hα light. The total absence of bright nebulosity in the right-hand photograph is to be noted. We draw attention to the fact that the shape of the North American continent is produced by dark nebulosity, especially in the "Gulf of Mexico" and in the "North Atlantic." The famous Pelican Nebula is shown in the left-hand photograph to the right of the North America Nebula. (Photographs by Dufay at the Haute Provence Observatory.)

are not isolated phenomena; they represent marked concentrations in an extended substratum of interstellar gas, which occupies much of the space between the stars in and near the central plane of our Milky Way system, especially in the spiral arms. There are various ways in which this gaseous substratum reveals itself to the observer. Modern photographic and spectrographic techniques have recently enabled us to record the faint outer extensions of the larger nebulae and to locate sometimes very extensive, very faint emission nebulae that had not been previously detected. The interstellar gas is also studied with the aid of certain sharp absorption lines observed in the spectra of distant galactic stars. And, finally, fresh evidence is now coming from radio astronomy, a rather young field on which we shall report in Chapter 8. Added interest in studies of emission nebulae arises through the discovery by Baade that the spiral arms in remote galaxies outside our own Milky Way system are most readily traced through alignments of patches of emission nebulosity. If we can locate the emission nebulae of our own Milky Way system and determine their true distances from the earth, then we may be able to trace the spiral arms in our own galaxy.

In 1937, Struve and Elvey constructed at the McDonald Observatory in Texas a powerful mountainside spectrograph, capable of recording spectral lines of very faint and extended emission nebulosities, which, before that time, had not been known to exist. More recently it has become possible to photograph these same nebulae,

Fig. 67. The region of Deneb. A Yerkes Observatory photograph made by W. W. Morgan with a short-focus 8-inch Schmidt telescope, showing the region of the North America Nebula and the Pelican Nebula, and the intricate nebulosity near Deneb. See also Fig. 125.

and others hitherto undetected, with the aid of fast red-sensitive photographic emulsions and special color filters. The new process of direct photography is basically a very simple one. Earlier attempts at direct photography of very faint emission nebulae had failed because the sky fog blackened the photographic plates before the faint nebulae had registered themselves sufficiently for detection. Astronomers reasoned that, if they could only suppress the sky fog without cutting out much of the nebular light, they should be able to take very long exposures with fast cameras and so record the faint nebulae. It should be remembered that the nebulae shine in the light of certain specific spectral lines, but that the sky fog on our photographs is produced partly by the aggregate light of all wavelengths from thousands of faint stars and by certain specific radiations present in the background light of the night sky. By a proper selection of color filters with narrow transmission bands, we should be able to cut out all but a small fraction of the continuous light from the background stars and also suppress most of the night-sky radiation, while permitting the light from one of the nebular emissions to pass

Fig. 68.   A bright fan-shaped nebula in Carina. The southern gaseous nebula NGC 3581, photographed in red light with the ADH telescope of the Boyden Station.

practically undiminished (Fig. 64). In practice this selective photography is achieved most readily with the use of the hydrogen emission line Hα, wavelength 6563 angstrom units, in the red part of the spectrum. The most effective filter is a Corning red filter combined with one of the remarkable interference filters made by Baird Associates at Cambridge, Massachusetts. The type of filter that has thus far been principally employed in work of this sort, transmits close to 90 percent of the Hα light of the nebulae, but almost no radiation is transmitted outside a band 50 angstrom units wide centered on Hα. With such a filter arrangement and with the fastest red-sensitive plates produced by Eastman Kodak, it has been found practicable to make exposures up to 4 hours with a camera operating at a focal ratio of 1.5.

The search for faint, extended emission nebulosities has proved so rewarding that in the past 5 years many observatories have participated in it. In the Soviet Union, Shajn and Miss Hase at the Simeis Observatory in the Crimea and Fessenkov at Alma Ata have taken remarkable photographs showing filamentary structure overlying large sections of the northern Milky Way. In France, Courtes and Dufay have worked in the same field, and in the United States some of the finest photographs have been made at the Yerkes and the McDonald Observatories, first in 1952 by W. W. Morgan, Sharpless, and Osterbrock and more recently by Morgan, Strömgren, and H. M. Johnson. The southern Milky Way has also re-

Fig. 69. Filamentary nebulosity. One of the several filamentary nebulae discovered and photographed by Shajn and associates at the Crimean Astrophysical Observatory in the U.S.S.R.

ceived its share of attention; the first surveys for the half of the Milky Way that is richest in emission nebulosity were made by Gum in Australia and by Bok, Bester, and Wade and also by Code and Houck from the Boyden Station in South Africa. All this work with relatively small wide-angle cameras has resulted in a fairly complete mapping of the sections in which emission nebulosity— including very weak emission—occurs over rather large areas of the sky.

The linear scales of the photographs made with the small search cameras are generally, however, too small to reveal the full detail of each nebulous structure and some of the finer features often remain undetected. Hence larger telescopes of fairly small focal ratios (and therefore of great light-gathering power) are used to reveal the full details of structure. In this connection the 48-inch Schmidt telescope of the Mount Palomar Observatory and the 32-inch Baker-Schmidt telescope of the Boyden Station, known as the Armagh-Dunsink-Harvard telescope, are proving very helpful for the charting of the northern and southern Milky Way. A Schmidt photograph covers an area of the sky at least 100 times that covered by the full moon and yet the scale of the photograph is sufficient to show the details of structure in the nebulous filaments. To round out the picture, we turn finally to the large reflectors, such as the 200-inch Hale and the 100-inch Hooker telescopes of the Mount Wilson and Palomar Observatories for the Northern Hemisphere and the 74-inch reflectors of the Radcliffe Observatory in South Africa and of the Commonwealth Observatory in Australia, which show the more conspicuous nebulae in all their glory and in finest detail.

Thus far the search for faint, extended emission nebulosities has been concentrated largely upon nebulae shining in the red light of the Hα line of hydrogen. We noted at the beginning of the present chapter that the Hα line originates usually as a by-product from the capture of a free electron by a single proton, a proton being the nucleus of a hydrogen atom. If we are right in supposing that this is the dominant process, then the observation of Hα is indicative of the presence of ionized hydrogen atoms, caught in the act of re-combination. In the professional jargon of the astrophysicist, the clouds of hydrogen that are largely ionized are called H(II) regions. The term was first introduced by Strömgren, who showed that H(II) regions should occur around O and B stars rich in ultraviolet radiation capable of ionizing the interstellar hydrogen. Strömgren finds that, for an average density of interstellar hydrogen of the order of one hydrogen atom per cubic centimeter, a B0 star will have sufficient ultraviolet radiation to ionize all the hydrogen to a distance of 100 light-years from the star. For the same hydrogen density, a very hot O star may produce complete ionization within a sphere of radius 500 light-years—resulting in a hydrogen-emission nebula of truly gigantic size. The supply of ultraviolet light and re-sultant ionizing power decreases rapidly as we proceed to the cooler stars. An A0 star with a still rather respectable surface temperature of the order of 11,000° will probably ionize a sphere with a radius of only 1.5 light-years, and the cooler stars will produce no appreci-able hydrogen ionization at all. It therefore causes little surprise that near almost every H(II) region one finds an O or B star that may be held responsible for exciting the nebular radiation.

We are really concerned with two varieties of regions of inter-stellar hydrogen. In the H(I) regions the atomic hydrogen is sup-posedly predominantly neutral, whereas in the H(II) regions the majority of the atoms are ionized. In the H(II) regions, the ionizing ultraviolet radiation from nearby stars is relatively plentiful, and the electrons are ejected at the time of ionization with sufficiently

Fig. 70(*a*).   The Milky Way in Scorpius in Hα light. The key chart shown in Fig. 70(*b*) indicates the positions of the principal gaseous nebulae in this section of the Milky Way. These
nebulae are part of an inner spiral arm of our Milky Way system. (Perkin- Zeiss camera, Boyden
Station.)

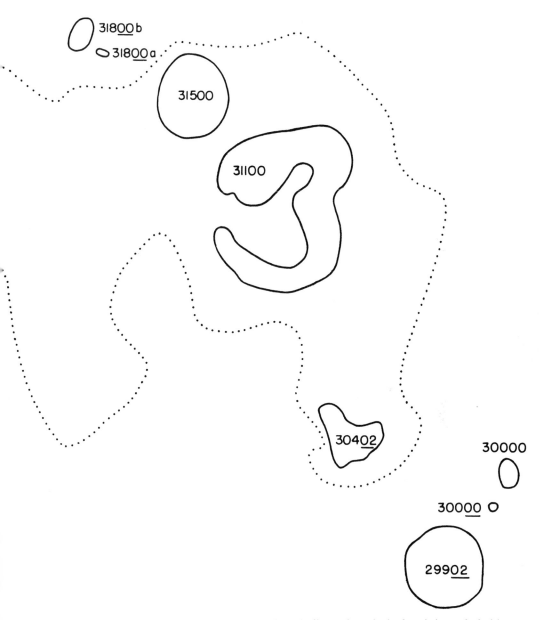

Fig. 70(*b*).   Key chart for Fig. 70(*a*). The full lines indicate the principal emission nebulosities shown in Fig. 70(*a*); the dotted line gives the outer boundary of detectable nebulosity. The numbers refer to the positions of the features in galactic coördinates. The first three figures are the longitudes, the last two the latitudes; underlining indicates negative latitudes. A section of the Sagittarius spiral arm can be traced diagonally from upper left to lower right in the diagram.

high speeds to produce equivalent temperatures in the interstellar gas of the order of 10,000°. In the H(I) regions ionization does not play much of a role and there is no process by which interstellar atoms may maintain the same high speed as for the H(II) regions. According to estimates by Spitzer and Savedoff, the speeds of the interstellar atoms in H(I) regions correspond to a temperature of 60° above the absolute zero, or on the centigrade scale more than 200° below the freezing point of water.

*   *

*

Instellar
Absorption
Lines

The interstellar gas reveals itself not only through the characteristic bright-line spectra of the emission nebulae, but also through certain sharp and narrow absorption lines found in the spectra of many distant stars. The discovery of the first absorption line goes back to 1904, when the German astronomer Hartmann showed that the absorption K line of ionized calcium (wavelength = 3933 angstroms) in the spectrum of the star Delta Orionis behaved in a very peculiar fashion. Delta Orionis is a blue star with a B0 spectrum and was recognized to be a spectroscopic binary. Hartmann found, however, that the wavelength of the K line did not vary at all in the course of the binary period. The hydrogen and helium lines in Delta Orionis were broad and fuzzy and varied, but its K line was sharp and distinct. Hartmann referred to the line as the "stationary" calcium line.

Stationary calcium lines have since been discovered in the spectra of many other early-type stars. In 1919 Miss Heger and Wright at the Lick Observatory found that the spectra of some early-type stars have strong stationary sodium lines, in addition to their stationary calcium lines. In all cases these lines were found to be sharp and distinct.

The interstellar origin of these absorption lines was first suggested by V. M. Slipher in 1909, but his suggestion unfortunately did not receive the attention it deserved and his views were not generally accepted until more than 15 years later. It was thought at first that the stationary lines originated in the immediate vicinity of the stars in whose spectra they are found. The researches of Plaskett and Struve proved that this explanation was incorrect. Theoretical investigations, especially those of Eddington and Rosseland, showed

Fig. 71.   The Milky Way in Scorpius; Hα light excluded. The photograph covers precisely the same area of the Milky Way shown in Fig. 70(a), but here a narrow-band Baird filter was used, selected to exclude practically all Hα radiation. The emission nebulae are either absent or very weak. (Perkin-Zeiss camera, Boyden Station.)

Fig. 72(*a*).   The Milky Way in Sagittarius in Hα light. The key chart shown in Fig. 72(*b*) indicates the position of the principal gaseous nebulae in this section of the Milky Way. The nebulae mark an extension of the inner spiral arm shown in Fig. 70(*a*). (Perkin-Zeiss camera, Boyden Station.)

NORTH

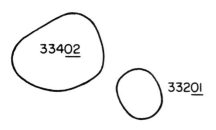

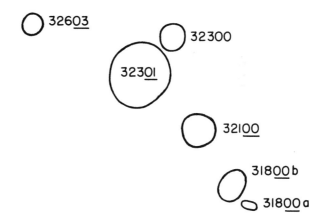

Fig. 72(*b*).   Key chart for Fig. 72(*a*). The marking system is the same as that in Fig. 70(*b*). A continuation of the spiral arm can be traced. Note that the features *a* and *b* at 31800 are shown on both charts.

further that stationary lines of calcium would naturally be observed if any gas were present in interstellar space. The total evidence left little doubt as to the interstellar origin of the stationary lines, and since 1930 they have generally been referred to as *interstellar lines*.

Adams and Dunham at the Mount Wilson Observatory have found interstellar absorption lines attributable to neutral calcium, neutral potassium, neutral iron, and ionized titanium in addition to the lines of ionized calcium and neutral sodium to which we have already referred (Figs. 77 and 78). All told, fifteen sharp interstellar absorption lines have been definitely identified. Dunham further found some sharp interstellar lines in the blue-violet part of the spectrum which for some time remained unidentified. McKellar of the Dominion Astrophysical Observatory in Canada proved that these lines arose from transitions between energy levels in simple molecular combinations of carbon, nitrogen, and hydrogen. Eleven lines of molecular origin have been definitely identified. Finally, Merrill of the Mount Wilson Observatory has given evidence for the presence of six broad and as yet unidentified interstellar absorption bands, the strongest at 4430 angstroms with an approximate width of more than 40 angstroms. It is not yet known how these broad bands are produced. The suggestion has been made that they may come from more complex molecules or from a transition stage in the formation of solid particles, but for the time being all this is frankly guesswork.

How do the observed interstellar lines originate? Suppose we take as an example the interstellar K line with a wavelength of 3933 angstroms, which can be produced only by the absorption of a light quantum of that wavelength by an ionized calcium atom in interstellar space. Since the atomic phenomena take place in a rather leisurely fashion in interstellar space, the ionized calcium atom will probably have settled down to its lowest energy level. Then there may by chance come along a stellar quantum of wavelength 3933 angstroms, just capable of temporarily exciting the calcium ion into a higher level of energy. Atomic physics teaches us that the calcium ion can stay in that blown-up state for only something like $1/10^7$ second and that then it returns to its original lowest energy level. The energy that was formerly absorbed is thereby released, but the new quantum of wavelength 3933 angstroms will go off in a direction different from that in which the previous one arrived. If we are looking at the spectrum of a certain star and there is ionized calcium

Fig. 73.   A gaseous nebula in Scorpius. The photograph shows the gaseous nebula near galactic
longitude 321°, latitude 0° (see also Fig. 70(*b*), where it is marked as 32100) in the constellation
Scorpius. North is at the top, east to the right, in this photograph taken with the Armagh-
Dunsink-Harvard telescope. (Boyden Station photograph by Bester.)

Fig. 74.   Nebula NGC 6334 and surroundings. A photograph in Hα light made by Bester with the ADH telescope of Boyden Station. The region shown is that of object *31800 b* in Figs. 70(*b*) and 72(*b*); see also Fig. 72(*a*). North is the upper right-hand corner; east is toward the lower right.

Fig. 75. A southern rim nebula. A photograph on a red-sensitive emulsion made by Bester with the Rockefeller reflector of Boyden Station. A fine example of a bright rim nebula. North is at the right; east is at the top.

Fig. 76.   The star Eta Carinae. The short-exposure Hα photograph of the densest portion of the Eta Carinae nebula (compare with frontispiece) shows us on a slightly enlarged scale the star Eta Carinae (very bright) and the intricate pattern of nebulosity immediately near the star. Note that in this photograph, as in Fig. 10, south is at the top, whereas in the frontispiece south is to the left. (Photograph by Thackeray, Radcliffe Observatory.)

between that star and us, then the interstellar calcium ions will absorb and scatter many of the quanta of wavelength 3933 angstroms, which would otherwise have reached our spectroscope; hence a dark K line appears in the spectrum of the star.

As yet little is known concerning the relative abundances of the various atoms in interstellar space. The first estimates were made by Dunham and more recent and improved values have been published by Strömgren and by Seaton. Hydrogen appears to be by far the most abundant element of interstellar space, and helium probably comes next, though we must admit that we do not possess at present a good estimate of the relative abundance of hydrogen and helium. Strömgren estimates that the abundance of oxygen is only 0.001 that of hydrogen, that of calcium 0.0001 that of hydrogen, and, further, that the abundance of sodium, potassium, titanium, and the interstellar molecules are even smaller than those of oxygen and calcium. If we were to analyze a sample of the interstellar gas we would almost certainly conclude it to be a mixture of hydrogen and helium, with mere traces of the other elements. It is interesting to note that, as far as we can tell, the relative abundances of the heavier elements are about the same in our sun, in the earth, and in interstellar space. But there is proportionally far less hydrogen on our earth than in the sun or in interstellar space. The reason for this state of affairs can be readily understood. The very light hydrogen atoms and molecules moved fast enough to escape the gravitational pull of the earth and only the hydrogen that was already combined with heavier atoms at the time our earth solidified was retained by our atmosphere.

* *

*

Cloud Structure and Galactic Structure

The interstellar gas shows considerable cloud structure. Until 1936, astrophysicists supposed that the interstellar gas was distributed smoothly through a thin layer near the central plane of the Milky Way, but in that year Beals, then of the Dominion Astrophysical Observatory in Canada, found evidence for multiplicity of some of the lines, indicating that more than one cloud of gas was contributing to the formation of the interstellar absorption lines in certain stars. Subsequent studies at high dispersion of the K line of ionized calcium were carried out by Adams at the Mount Wilson Observatory. He showed that more than 30 percent of the stars examined by him had double or triple interstellar K lines, and a K line with four components was found for four stars. It may be assumed that every observed component of the K line is produced by a separate and distinct interstellar cloud. The separation between the components is caused by the difference in the Doppler shift produced by different radial velocities of the separate clouds relative to the sun.

In recent years Münch of the California Institute of Technology has found many stars that show multiple interstellar lines (Fig. 79); one of his spectra shows as many as seven components, every one of them indicative of a separate interstellar cloud between our sun and the star in question, each cloud with a different radial velocity relative to the sun. Münch's observations present most convincing

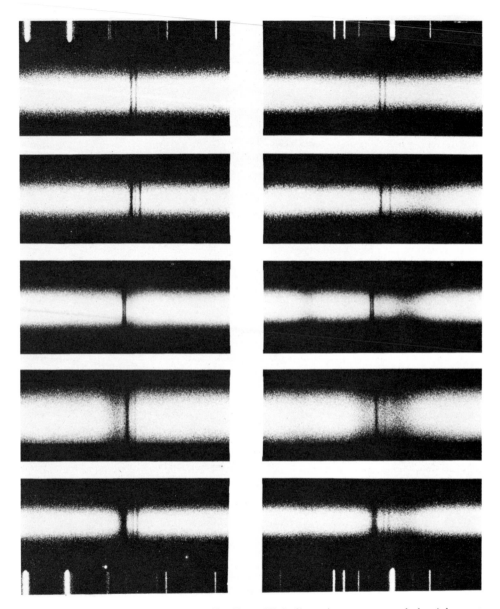

Fig. 77.   Multiple interstellar lines. High-dispersion spectra made by Adams at
Mount Wilson Observatory show many instances of multiple interstellar lines.
This multiplicity indicates the presence of distinct interstellar clouds, each moving
at its own peculiar rate.

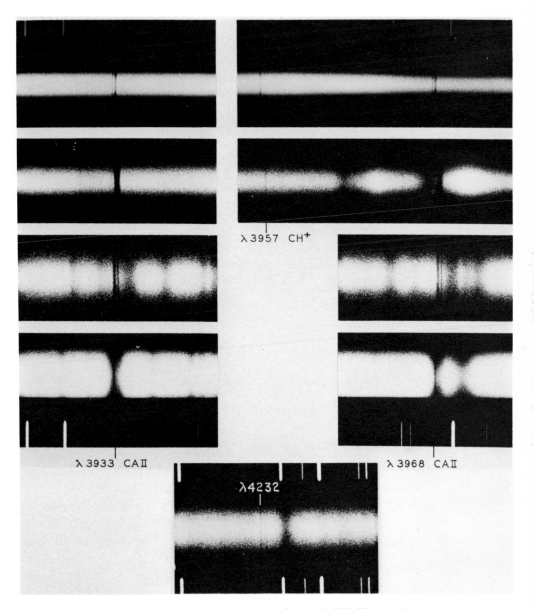

Fig. 78. Interstellar lines of ionized calcium and of ionized CH. The marked sharp lines are examples of interstellar absorption lines—several of them multiple lines—discovered by Adams. (Mount Wilson photograph.)

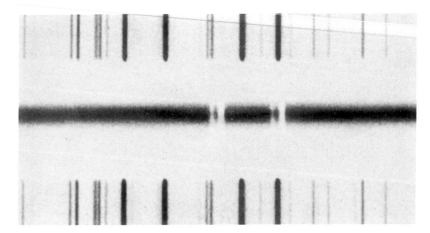

Fig. 79.   Interstellar sodium lines. The spectrum of star No. 12953 in the Henry
Draper *Catalogue* photographed by Münch with the coudé spectrograph of the 200-
inch Hale telescope. The black central band is the negative impression of the
stellar spectrum and the white lines in the dark band are two components of the
D_1 line of neutral sodium and two components of the D_2 line also due to neutral
sodium. There are two components to each line because between the star and our
sun there are two clouds producing neutral sodium absorption, one of which, with
a radial velocity of approach of 55 km/sec, gives the weaker component (to the
left) of each pair, the other, with a radial velocity of approach of 7 km/sec, yielding the stronger component (to the right) of each pair. The lines at the top and
bottom are from the comparison spectrum imprinted during the exposure. They
are emission lines and hence appear black in the negative print. The star is
of spectral class A1 and luminosity class Ia. It is at an estimated distance of 7000
light-years, and it so happens that, in the limited stretch of spectrum shown, there are
no stellar absorption lines present.

evidence for the cloud structure of the interstellar gaseous medium.
We note here that the multiple interstellar lines found by Münch
occur even in the spectra of some stars at considerable distances
from the galactic plane, thus suggesting that at least some wisps of
interstellar gas have sufficient speeds at right angles to the plane of
the Milky Way to reach considerable heights above or below the
plane. We shall see in Chapter 8 that the great majority of the interstellar clouds discovered by Münch are near the central plane
and fit nicely into the accepted spiral pattern of our galaxy.

The interstellar gas partakes in the general rotation of our galaxy.
This fact has been established by the researches of Plaskett and
Pearce at the Dominion Astrophysical Observatory. Shortly after
Oort had suggested that the radial velocities of distant stars should
vary in a double sine wave according to galactic longitude, Plaskett

and Pearce undertook to measure the radial velocities of several hundred faint, and hence distant, early-type stars and made a successful check of the theory of galactic rotation. The interstellar K line was measurable on many of the spectrograms of Plaskett and Pearce. When the radial velocities determined from the measurements of the interstellar K line were plotted against the galactic longitude of the stars, the results showed very clearly the familiar effects of galactic rotation. The striking difference was that the range of the double wave for the stars was approximately twice the range for the velocities from the K line. The conclusion that Plaskett and Pearce drew from their curves was that the interstellar K line in a given star yielded on the average a radial velocity corresponding to the halfway point between the star and the observer.

The early measurements based on interstellar lines seemed to suggest that interstellar calcium atoms are distributed rather uniformly near the galactic plane. Because of the discovery of multiple interstellar absorption lines in the spectra of many stars, this simple picture has been abandoned. We visualize the interstellar gaseous medium as consisting primarily of a relatively flat layer of individual gas clouds, with a thin galactic substratum possibly connecting them. Each cloud moves around the center of the galaxy in an approximately circular orbit. On the average the actual velocity of a cloud differs from the circular velocity of galactic rotation by $\pm$ 8 kilometers per second. With very few exceptions—which we shall note later on—the clouds that produce the observed interstellar absorption lines are located in the spiral arm that contains our sun.

7

Dark Nebulae and Cosmic Dust

For the part of our galaxy within two or three thousand light-years of the sun and earth, about two-thirds of all matter is in the stars and the remainder is in the gas and dust of interstellar space. According to the best current estimates, at least 99 percent of this interstellar matter is gaseous and the tiny solid interstellar pellets account for the remaining 1 percent. In the present chapter we shall be concerned with observable effects produced by the interstellar dust particles and we shall see that much can be learned about their composition, approximate dimensions, and distribution in and outside the cosmic clouds. Clouds of cosmic dust reveal themselves in a variety of ways. Sometimes they shine like faintly luminous nebulae, but more often they are seen as apparent star voids through which the stars beyond are faintly seen. Finally, we can often detect the presence of intervening cosmic dust by the reddening and polarization effects in the light of very remote stars.

*   *

*

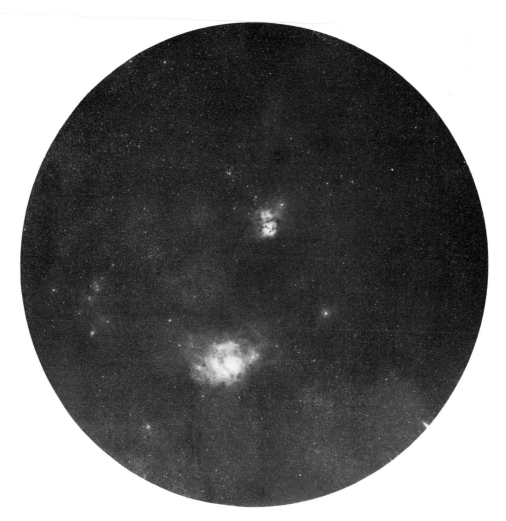

Fig. 80.   Messier 8 and the Trifid Nebula. Two of the finest gaseous nebulae north of the galactic center. Note the overlying pattern of dark matter. (ADH photograph, Boyden Station.)

Reflection
Nebulae

Until 1912, it was generally supposed that all bright nebulae would show spectra similar to that of the Nebula of Orion, that is, bright-line spectra. Then V. M. Slipher announced that the nebula associated with the Pleiades gives an absorption spectrum, very much like that of the brightest stars in the Pleiades cluster. Other nebulae were found to behave in a similar fashion. There are apparently two kinds of bright nebulae, one with bright-line (emission) spectra,

the variety of which we wrote in the preceding chapter, the other
with dark-line (absorption) spectra similar to those shown by the
majority of the stars. Hubble showed that emission nebulae are
generally near very hot stars with spectral types O, B0, or B1, but
he found that the nebulae with absorption spectra are associated
with cooler stars.

This second variety of nebula is generally called a *reflection nebula,*
since it shines in the reflected and scattered light from the star that
renders it visible. It is truly a starlit cosmic cloud.

The reflection nebulae generally show no emission features because the stars that cause them to shine lack a sufficient supply of
ultraviolet radiation to produce luminescence through ionization
followed by recombination. The absence of marked absorption features in most emission nebulae is a bit more difficult to explain. It
is probably due to the fact that there are very few solid particles
in the hottest emission nebulae. First, the radiation pressure from
the hot stars would tend to drive such particles away from the
brightest parts of the nebulae and, second, the particles that do not
escape are probably evaporated.

Struve, Greenstein, and Henyey have made some very careful
studies of the physical properties of reflection nebulae. From the
observed surface brightnesses of these nebulae they deduce that the
particles that produce the reflection are excellent reflectors. There
is nothing gray or grimy about the dust of interstellar space. The
cosmic grains represent in their reflective power tiny hailstones
much more than pulverized dust; in the language of the astronomer, the cosmic particles appear to have a high albedo, comparable
to that of snow, though perhaps not quite so high. The indicated
high reflectivity for these particles suggests that they are not primarily metallic. It seems most likely that they are icelike small
grains composed of simple molecular compounds of the lighter elements, such as carbon, nitrogen, oxygen, and of course hydrogen.

Important conclusions regarding the probable size of the particles
may be drawn from comparative studies of the colors of these reflection nebulae and the colors of the responsible stars. We are all
familiar with the observation that the light of the setting sun is
reddened considerably in its passage through the atmosphere and,
in turn, that the scattered light from the sun produces the blue
aspect of our earthly sky. The difference between the color of our
sun and the blue of our sky is explained by the phenomenon called

Fig. 81. The emission nebula Messier 8. A photograph made with the Crossley reflector of Lick Observatory. This is the same emission nebula shown in the lower half of Fig. 80. Several dark markings are of roughly circular shape and these are referred to as "globules."

Rayleigh scattering. The actual scattering of the sun's light in our atmosphere is produced by particles with dimensions considerably smaller than the wavelength of visible light, probably mostly molecules. The reflection nebulae are somewhat bluer than the stars whose light they reflect, but the color difference is by no means so marked as is the case of our sun and the daytime sky. From the observed differences in color between reflection nebulae and illuminating stars, we deduce that the scattering particles have radii of the order of 0.00001 inch.

*   *

*

Dark

Nebulae If a cloud of gas and dust is present in interstellar space it will not appear as a diffuse nebula unless there is a bright star in or near the cloud. The exciting stars and nebulous clouds are generally not

Fig. 82. The Rosette Nebula. A photograph in red light of the Rosette Nebula in Monoceros, made with the 48-inch Palomar Schmidt telescope.

physically connected and it is hardly surprising that we find many interstellar clouds that are not near a suitable star. Such clouds will, however, absorb and scatter the light from the stars beyond them and they will be distinguishable as dark nebulae against the bright background of the Milky Way.

Dark nebulae are not conspicious objects for visual observers. They are uninteresting regions devoid of stars, or with fewer stars than normal, and an observer will pass them by in favor of fields that are rich in stars. Sir William Herschel was the first astronomer who seriously considered the implications of the vacancies along the Milky Way, and it was also Sir William who noticed that the vacancies occur frequently in the vicinity of bright nebulae. It was not until a century after Sir William's observations that Barnard and Wolf succeeded in proving from their Milky Way photographs that many vacancies were caused by obscuring clouds rather than by holes in the Milky Way.

We reproduce in this book several photographs of bright diffuse nebulae. The many irregularities in the distribution of light in the bright nebulae and the related irregularities in the distribution of the faint stars suggest that many of the bright nebulae serve as backgrounds against which can be observed the numerous dark nebulae of various sizes that lie between the bright nebulae and our earth. Among the finest examples are the Great Nebula near Eta Carinae (frontispiece) and the emission nebula known as Messier 8 (Figs. 80 and 81). Lanes of obscuring material obviously overlie much of the bright structure and, most noticeable of all, we observe numerous small dark spots seen projected against the bright background. These spots are seen in the same position from night to night and from year to year and they are surely small obscuring clouds. Some of these spots have a wind-blown, turbulent appearance, while others — generally referred to as *globules* — have a markedly round appearance (Figs. 82, 83, and 84).

There are several other instances of real association between bright and dark nebulosity; the Horsehead Nebula in Orion is a good example of such association. The ectoplasmic glow around the horse's head emanates from the bright nebulosity. The horse's head is a part of the large dark nebula that covers most of the upper half of Fig. 47. If the dark nebula suggests an ominous thundercloud, the bright nebula is the sunlit edge. The photograph of the Horsehead Nebula shows clearly the power of the dark nebula to

Fig. 83. Globules in the Rosette Nebula. An enlarged portion of Fig. 82, showing numerous globules, first noted here by Minkowski.

Fig. 84.   Dark markings in the southern Milky Way. Thackeray at the Radcliffe Observatory first noted the remarkable dark markings shown here, which are probably very similar to the dark globules.

absorb the light of the stars beyond it. If we compare the number of stars in two squares of equal size, one above, the other below the horsehead, we count at least ten times as many stars in the first square as in the second square. One can have little doubt about the power of this particular dark nebula to dim the light of the stars that lie behind it.

The Coalsack (Fig. 86), in the Southern Hemisphere, is one of the most striking dark nebulae in a region devoid of bright nebulosity. Largely because of the contrast with the brilliant Milky Way

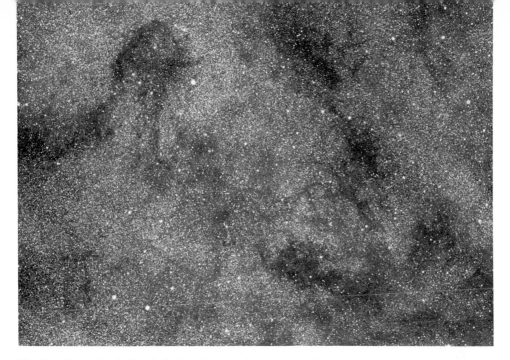

Fig. 85. Irregular dark nebulosity. An irregular network of dark nebulosity over-lies this region a few degrees south of the galactic center. (ADH photograph, Boyden Station.)

Fig. 86. The Coalsack and the Southern Cross. To the right and above the dark nebula known as the Southern Coalsack, the four stars of the Southern Cross can be seen. The bright nebula on the right is the Eta Carinae nebula, with north toward the upper edge of the photograph. (Boyden Station photograph.)

surrounding it, the Coalsack appears to the visual observer as an intensely black cloud. Telescopic observations will readily reveal the presence of numerous faint stars in the apparent inky darkness of the Coalsack. A long-exposure photograph, such as that reproduced in Fig. 86, shows that there are still on the average one-third as many faint stars in the Coalsack as in an adjacent area of the same size. It is not really so black as it appeared at first. In the same way, the sunspots appear black against the sun's disk although they are actually bright. The Coalsack nebula stood for many years as the finest example of a dark nebula free from bright nebulosity. In 1938 a minute flare of bright nebulosity in the Coalsack was found by Lindsay at the Boyden Station, and others have since been noted by Gum, but these are distant gas clouds viewed through the Coalsack.

Some of the finest photographs of dark nebulae were made many years ago by Barnard of the Yerkes and Lick Observatories. Figure 87 shows the North America Nebula, so named by Wolf of Heidelberg. The photograph gives a striking illustration of the association between bright and dark nebulosity. The "United States" is a conspicuous bright nebula, the "Gulf of Mexico" is one of the densest portions of the surrounding dark nebula. From the large numbers of faint stars that shine through the bright nebula, it is apparent that the bright nebulosity is more transparent than the dark portions.

Another striking photograph by Barnard is reproduced in Fig. 88. The dark nebula near the star Rho Ophiuchi is probably part of the giant dark nebula in Ophiuchus, which according to the evidence from the distribution of stars and faint galaxies covers an area of 1000 square degrees. The great body of the nebular mass lies from 5° to 20° north of the galactic circle and lacks the background of faint stars to render it conspicuous. The low-latitude "tentacles" of the Ophiuchus nebula, however, are seen projected against some of the richest portions of the Milky Way and the nebula near Rho Ophiuchi is one of the tentacles.

What can we learn about the extent, distance, and composition of a dark nebula? Information on the first two points can be obtained from star counts in and around the nebula. The counts for two areas of similar size, one in the dark nebula, the other in a neighboring unobscured region, will generally agree for the brighter stars. As we count to fainter magnitudes we soon come to a point where the counts in the obscured area fall below those for the comparison area. The percentage deficiency will generally increase as

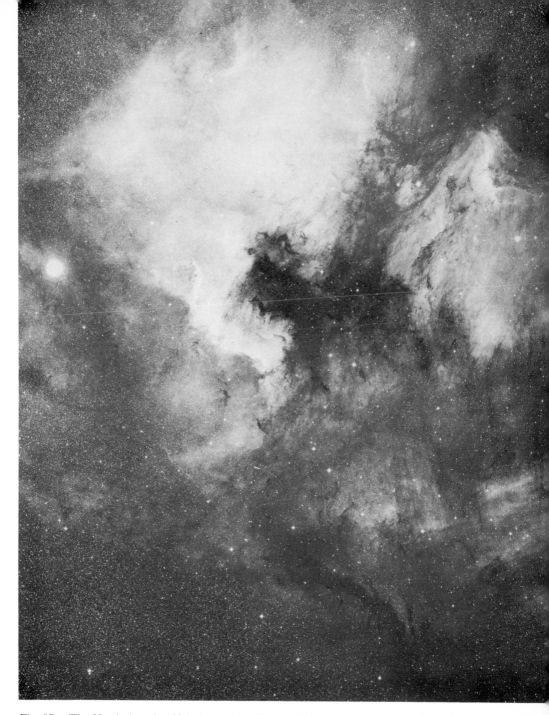

Fig. 87. The North America Nebula and the Pelican Nebula. A reproduction from the National Geographic Society–Palomar Observatory Sky Survey with the 48-inch Schmidt telescope. Compare with Fig. 66.

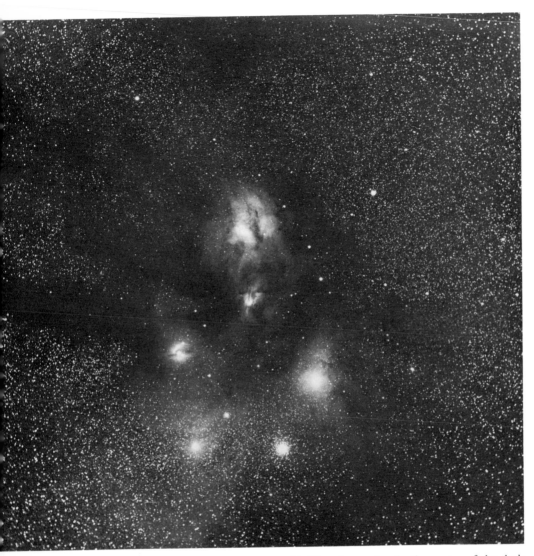

Fig. 88.   The dark nebula near Rho Ophiuchi. The obscuration in the center of the dark nebula amounts to approximately eight magnitudes of dimming. Near the edge of the pronounced obscuration, where two distant globular clusters can be seen on the photograph—a small one below the center and a larger one to the right of it and below—the obscuration amounts to only a little over one magnitude. Most of the bright nebulosity is of the reflection variety. The cosmic dust is strongly concentrated at a distance of 700 light-years. (From a photograph by Barnard at Mount Wilson Observatory made with the 10-inch Bruce camera of Yerkes Observatory.)

Fig. 89. Dark nebula in Scorpius-Sagittarius. The dark marking is at the border between Sagittarius and Scorpius. This same marking is also shown in Fig. 2, but in the present reproduction north is at the top but west is to the right. (Enlargement from a photograph with the ADH telescope of Boyden Station.)

Fig. 90. A small dark nebula in Sagittarius, photographed with the 100-inch Hooker reflector of Mount Wilson Observatory. Note the star cluster to the left of the dark marking.

fainter stars are included in our counts, but will finally become constant. The apparent magnitude for which the deficiency begins to be noticeable gives us some idea about the approximate distance of the dark nebula; the percentage deficiency for the faintest magnitudes is a good measure of the total obscuration caused by the cloud.

Wolf was one of the first astronomers to realize the value of star counts for the study of dark nebulae (Figs. 91 and 92). Statistical methods for the analysis of such star counts were developed by Pannekoek. The large spread in the absolute magnitudes of the stars of all kinds that make up general star counts renders it difficult to compute accurate distances of dark nebulae, but Pannekoek's method of analysis tells us at least whether the absorbing cloud is at 200, 600, or 1500 light-years from the sun. Pannekoek showed further that counts to faint limits gave very precise information on the total absorption of the nebulae.

The Coalsack, for instance, is caused by a dark cloud at roughly 400 light-years from our sun. That is right next door as galactic distances go. The total absorption of the cloud averages a little more than one magnitude, but in some dense portions it is as high as three magnitudes.

Estimated distances and absorptions are now available for the dust clouds in all major centers of local obscuration. In the Rift of

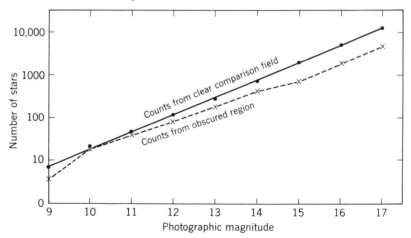

Fig. 91. Wolf curves for a dark nebula in Cygnus. Star counts by Franklin at Harvard have yielded these curves for a dark nebula seen superposed on the star cloud in Cygnus. The solid curve gives the counts for an unobscured comparison field and the broken curve the counts for the obscured field. The quantities plotted vertically are the numbers of stars between photographic apparent magnitudes $m - \frac{1}{2}$ and $m + \frac{1}{2}$, reduced to an area of 1 square degree of the sky.

the Milky Way, the dark nebulae in Aquila and southward seem to be all relatively near the sun, with estimated distances of the order of 500 light-years; for the part of the Rift in Cygnus the distances are more of the order of 2000 to 3000 light-years. The large dark nebula in Taurus is again nearby (500 light-years), but to the south we find in Orion, Monoceros, Puppis, and Vela a connected system of not-quite-so-thick dark nebulae at 2000 light-years from the sun. The Coalsack, at 400 light-years, is again one of the nearer nebulae.

General star counts alone tell us a good deal about the distance and absorption of a given dark nebula, but even with improved methods of analysis the results remain relatively uncertain because of the great spread in absolute magnitude of the stars. For definitive research on dark nebulae, we therefore turn to statistical studies based upon spectra and preferably also on colors of faint stars. From the spectral statistics alone, we obtain improved values for the distances of the dark nebulae. The colors of the faint stars of known spectral type enable us to investigate in addition the extent to which the starlight has been reddened in its passage through the dark nebulae.

The first extensive study of the effect of a dark nebula on the colors of faint stars observed through it was made in the early 1930's by the Swedish astronomer Schalén, who found that, while the starlight is definitely reddened in its passage through the nebula, the amount of reddening is rather small. The degree of reddening depends almost entirely on the average dimensions of the cosmic dust particles in the nebulae. Schalén concluded that the particles that are the most effective absorbers are tiny cosmic grains with diameters of about one hundred-thousandth of an inch. Unfortunately, the observed coloring effects in the spectra of stars ob-

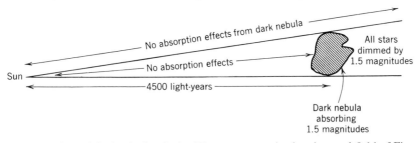

Fig. 92.   A model of a dark nebula. The star counts in the obscured field of Fig. 91 can be represented by assuming the presence of a dark nebula with a total photographic absorption of 1.5 magnitudes at a distance of 4500 light-years. (Franklin's results.)

served through dark nebulae do not permit a clear-cut decision between icelike and metallic particles. Schalén made the at the time apparently rather reasonable assumption that the tiny dust specks are metallic, notably compounds of iron, zinc, or copper. Much has happened since the time when Schalén did his pioneer work. It has been proved that hydrogen and the lighter elements are probably very much more abundant in space than the heavy metals. Also, the reflectivity studies of bright reflection nebulae, about which we have spoken in the preceding section, have demonstrated that the majority of interstellar particles are probably composed of carbon, nitrogen, oxygen, and hydrogen. Most astrophysicists are now inclined to favor the hypothesis of a nonmetallic composition for the cosmic grains, though serious doubts have again arisen since the discovery of interstellar polarization, about which we shall speak later in this chapter. It does seem as though on the whole the distribution of varieties of particles and of particle sizes is fairly uniform throughout our galactic system. Some years ago, there seemed to be certain sections of the sky, notably near the Orion Nebula, for which the law of reddening, that is, the law expressing the variation of percentage reddening with wavelength, differs from the average law. A recent study by Mlle. Divan has disproved that contention and no marked discrepancies remain.

*   *

*

Ratio of Gas to Dust   The coexistence of interstellar gas and cosmic dust in many sections of the Milky Way has led astrophysicists to ask if a constant ratio is maintained between the average densities of gas and dust everywhere in space. Attempts have been made to answer this question either through purely theoretical deductions or by trying to secure critical optical or radio observations.

The purely theoretical approach has been explored most thoroughly by Spitzer and Savedoff at the Princeton Observatory. If the gas component has a total density equal to at least 10 times and probably 100 times the dust component, then it can be shown that the gas should literally drag the tiny dust particles along with it. The dust becomes then little more than a tracer for the gas and a fairly constant ratio between the densities of interstellar gas and dust might be maintained everywhere. One recognizes, however, that this mixing in constant proportions may extend over only fairly small volumes and that there are many factors that may produce a different mixture for two widely separated points in our Milky Way system. Theoretical studies are helpful as a guide to the interpretation of observations, but theory alone cannot give a solution to the problem.

Unfortunately, the second approach, that of observation with the aid of either photographic and spectroscopic or radio techniques has not provided a final clear-cut answer. Observations with conventional telescopes yield no clue, for the simple reason that the neutral hydrogen atoms in the cold interstellar clouds send out no detectable radiation in the photographic, visual, or red range. The gas will betray its presence only by the radio radiation from neutral hydrogen with a wavelength of 21 centimeters, about which we shall report in Chapter 8.

Studies of the radio radiation from neutral hydrogen have been made especially by Lilley and others with the radio telescope at Harvard's Agassiz Station. Lilley found that the large Taurus complex of dark nebulosity is a region for which the intensity of the 21-centimeter radiation is considerably greater than the average for its galactic latitude. Where there exists a very large complex of cosmic dust, there is also a greater concentration than average of interstellar hydrogen gas. Lilley has shown that for the Taurus complex the average density of the neutral hydrogen gas is about 100 times the average calculated density of the cosmic dust. This is a great deal of neutral hydrogen for each dust particle, but the figure should be contrasted with that for the average point near the galactic plane; here the total amount of gas and dust per cubic centimeter is considerably smaller than in the Taurus complex, and the corresponding ratio of gas and dust density is more nearly 300 or 500 to 1.

At the Agassiz Station, Bok, Lawrence, and Menon have investigated the 21-centimeter radiation in the smallest and densest dark nebulae accessible by present radio methods. They find that the 21-centimeter radiation from the densest dark nebulae inside a complex of gas and dust is not perceptibly greater than that reaching us from the less concentrated parts of the same complex. Their result confirms that of an earlier preliminary investigation by van de Hulst, Muller, and Oort of Leiden. It seems therefore as though on the large scale the dust complexes represent regions of excessive neutral hydrogen content, but that on the small scale there exist extra-dense dust clouds of modest dimensions that do not possess added neutral hydrogen.

This conclusion, if substantiated by further research—especially with very large radio telescopes, which should permit the study of smaller and denser dark nebulae than are now accessible to study by radio methods—will have an important bearing on problems of cosmic evolution. For it is obvious that the evolution of a dense cloud consisting mainly of cosmic dust will be very different from that of a cloud with 100 times as much hydrogen as dust. But, as happens so often in scientific research, there is a joker hidden in our deck of cards. By radio methods we now test only the presence or absence of neutral atomic hydrogen. There may be in the densest dust clouds very little atomic neutral hydrogen but much molecular hydrogen; our radio or optical techniques fail to give a direct test to check on the presence of hydrogen molecules in dust clouds. Pure theory in this case is of very little assistance. For the time being, we consider it most probable that the densest dark nebulae do not have an excessive hydrogen content, but there remains the possibility of a considerable amount of as yet undetectable molecular hydrogen.

*   *

*

The Cosmic Dust

In our search for interstellar material we have paid much attention to the obscuring clouds. What about the regions where faint stars shine in great numbers and where there is no direct evidence for the presence of intervening dust? We have learned to expect along the Milky Way the telltale absorption lines from the interstellar gas. But the atoms of hydrogen, calcium, and sodium can only absorb light of certain very special wavelengths and the presence of the gas will not lead to any general scattering or reddening of the light of distant stars. If we find scattering or reddening effects for distant objects outside the obvious obscuring clouds we shall have to leave room on our census blanks for a general haze of cosmic dust.

If we photograph any region of the sky that is at least 25° away from the galactic belt we shall generally find some images of faint spiral or elliptical nebulae on our plate. We refer to these as "galaxies" because they are separate stellar systems, some of which are probably not unlike our own Milky Way system. They begin to appear on 1-hour photographs with a 10-inch refractor; a 3-hour exposure with a 16- or 24-inch telescope will show sometimes hundreds of these galaxies. They appear in abundance on all regular photographs with large reflectors taken outside of the Milky Way plane.

If we photograph regions along the band of the Milky Way, even long exposures with the most powerful telescopes may not bring out any of these nebular images. What does this mean? Can it be that there are no faint galaxies in those directions, or are they cut off from our view by a general interstellar absorption? There can now be little doubt that the haze is to blame. The universe of galaxies has already been explored to distances of 500,000,000 light-years and it would simply be too presumptuous to assume that our home galaxy, with its diameter of scarcely 100,000 light-years, could somehow determine the whereabouts of its fellow galaxies. There are probably distant galaxies in all directions. Those along the galactic circle are hidden from our view by the interstellar material in and near the central plane of our own galaxy.

Now that we recognize the presence of an all-pervading cosmic haze close to the central plane of the Milky Way, we should like to know by how much on the average the light of a star in the Milky Way at a distance of, say, 5000 light-years is dimmed through the haze. There are two basically different approaches to this problem.

In the first approach, we depend on objects of known intrinsic brightness and estimate their distances by two methods, one basically trigonometric and hence not affected by interstellar absorption, the other entirely based on brightness measurements and hence having the full effect of the dimming of the starlight between the group of stars we consider and the earth. In the first method, one depends entirely on a parallax determined either from proper motions or, through galactic rotation effects, from radial velocities. The average distance thus obtained should be independent of the intervening absorption. In the second method, one calculates the mean distances of the group, neglecting interstellar absorption, on the assumption of a mean absolute magnitude M, by the formula

$$5 \log d = (m - M) + 5,$$

where m is the average apparent magnitude as measured directly and M the mean absolute magnitude. This formula should really contain a correction term for the absorption effect, and by neglecting it we erroneously place the stars too far away. We can then see how much absorption we must assume in order to bring the two derived distances into agreement.

Trumpler found indications for an average dimming in the photographic range of the order of one magnitude near the galactic circle and at a distance of 5000 light-years from the sun. Rather comparable values have been derived from studies of galactic-rotation effects in radial velocities of distant stars like the Cepheid variables, notably by Joy. The geometrical methods give even at best only averages of absorption. While such averages hold considerable interest, they give us little or no information about the absorption characteristics for a given direction in the Milky Way. For, as we have already noted, irregularity is one of the primary characteristics for the distribution of the interstellar dust that makes up the cosmic haze.

For the study of the absorption along a given line of sight, we prefer at present methods that give the space reddening suffered by individual distant stars. The first derived quantity, the color excess, is a measure of the amount of reddening produced by the obscuring matter between the observer on the earth and a particular star. From the amount of reddening we may then derive the total amount of photographic absorption by which the star's magnitude is changed.

A few general comments about space reddening are in order before we describe precisely how it is measured and what we learn from these measures. It is not difficult to prove that space reddening is a general phenomenon. Its effect is shown dramatically in Fig. 93, in which two photographs by Smith with the 60-inch Rockefeller reflector of Boyden Station are reproduced one above the other. In the lower photograph, which was made on a blue-sensitive emulsion, the star field and the globular cluster are only dimly seen, whereas on the upper photograph, made on a red-sensitive emulsion, the globular cluster stands out clearly and the star field looks richer. Baade adjusted the exposure times of the two photographs so that star images of equal size and density were obtained in the upper and lower photographs for stars of spectral type somewhere between F5 and G0, that is, for stars with true colors not unlike the color of our sun. Obviously the globular cluster and the field stars are all considerably reddened by interstellar

Fig. 93. Effects of interstellar reddening. The upper photograph is a reproduction of an infrared photograph made with the 60-inch Rockefeller reflector of Boyden Station; the lower photograph is of the same region in the usual blue light. The thick overlying screen of interstellar obscuration hides completely the globular cluster in blue light, but in the infrared the absorption is sufficiently reduced to permit us to see clearly a distant globular cluster.

obscuration. In some cases the effects of space reddening can even be observed visually. Observers with large reflectors who do research on the colors of B stars naturally develop the habit of checking upon the identification at the eyepiece of the telescope of a given B star by noting the marked blue-white color for the B stars, as contrasted with the more yellow or reddish color for other stars. But when we look at faint B stars in the general direction of the galactic center many of them appear yellowish, or some even reddish.

We showed in Chapter 2 how we can measure in a quantative way the amount of interstellar reddening as it affects the color of a given star. To do so we measure the color index as observed with the aid of the photoelectric photometer and then compare it with the true or intrinsic color index of the star for its spectral type, that is, the color index the star would have had in the absence of any space-reddening effects. The difference between the observed and the intrinsic color index is called the *color excess;* it is equal to the difference between the observed color index of the star and its intrinsic color index, expressed in magnitudes. The color excess is, therefore, a convenient figure to express the amount of reddening produced by the interstellar haze. But how can we pass from the color excess to an estimate of the total absorption? From studies of the wavelength dependence of the space reddening in selected bright stars, it has been possible to deduce how the reddening varies with wavelength in any particular star. If we once know the wavelengths that our filters transmit, we may derive with considerable certainty the factor by which the color excess should be multiplied if we wish to obtain the total absorption for photographic light.

To obtain information on the space reddening for the vicinity of the sun, we turn naturally to the B5 to A2 stars, which are found in abundance in the sky; from them we may learn much about interstellar absorption along the belt of the Milky Way for distances of the order of a few hundred to 5000 light-years from the sun. Most of the earlier studies were done photographically, but in recent years photoelectric calibration has become the custom. The most extensive studies of the space reddening of A stars have been carried out by McCuskey and his associates at Warner and Swasey Observatory, by Bok and Olmsted at Harvard, and by Kharadze and his associates at the Abastumani Observatory in the Soviet Union. From the observed degree of space reddening for various sections of the Milky Way, one deduces that the average dimming suffered by a light ray from a star close to the galactic circle comes to about 1 magnitude for path lengths of 3000 to 5000 light-years, but in certain directions much greater dimming is found.

The first accurate and still the most extensive survey of photoelectric colors of O and B stars along the Milky Way was completed by Stebbins, Huffer, and Whitford in 1939 at the University of Wisconsin and the Mount Wilson Observatory. Their basic list contains precise photoelectric colors for 1332 O and B stars. Because of their great intrinsic brightness, bright O and B stars are very distant objects and they are therefore quite suitable for work on space reddening. The research has been extended and continued by many workers in the field in both Northern and Southern Hemispheres. For the majority of O and B stars we now possess precise determinations of color excess and of spectral absolute magnitudes on the Morgan-Keenan-Kellman system. Thus a wealth of observational material on space reddening is available.

Highly reddened stars prevail in some sections of the Milky Way, in particular for the region of the galactic center. Bok and van Wijk found one faint B star in an obscured field not far from the direction of the galactic center which was so reddened that its estimated total photographic absorption is close to 6.5 magnitudes. In other words, this tenth-magnitude B star might have been a fairly conspicuous star, photographically between the third and fourth magnitude, if it had not been for the obscuration between the star and our sun. Space reddening is generally much less marked elsewhere than for the direction of the galactic center, but, to the best of our knowledge, all faint stars directly along the Milky Way do show measurable effects of space reddening. This suggests that nowhere

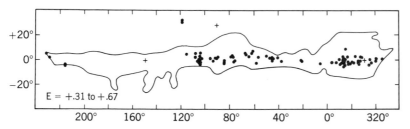

Fig. 94.   Highly reddened stars. The distribution along the Milky Way of stars with color excesses of the order of at least half a magnitude. The irregular curves outline Hubble's Zone of Avoidance, the belt along the Milky Way for which the absence of observed faint galaxies suggests considerable interstellar absorption. (Data from Stebbins, Huffer, and Whitford.)

along the Milky Way is there a direction totally free from the general haze. Figure 94 shows the galactic distribution of some of the most reddened stars found in the survey of Stebbins, Huffer, and Whitford. Very highly reddened B stars are apparently absent between 120° and 210°, the region away from the galactic center, but they are very numerous for the region between galactic longitude 320° and 0°, which includes the galactic center.

In recent years much attention has been given to color studies of distant Cepheid variables of the southern Milky Way. At the Commonwealth Observatory in Australia Eggen and Kron from the United States, along with Gascoigne of the Canberra staff, have studied the Cepheids of our own galaxy and in the Magellanic Clouds. Research on the basis of photoelectric and photographic material from South Africa is in progress in Holland (Oosterhoff and Walraven), Great Britain (Stibbs) and the United States (Irwin, Bok and Olmsted). Gascoigne has made the rather startling suggestion that probably all of the Cepheids observed in our galactic system are considerably reddened and that we observe unreddened Cepheids only in the Magellanic Clouds. Now that agreement appears in sight with regard to the absolute magnitudes of the Cepheids, they become the most useful type of object for the study of space reddening—and they should also play an important role in future studies of galactic rotation.

Faint and distant globular clusters have already come in for their share of attention. Stebbins and Whitford have measured photoelectric colors for all those within reach from the Mount Wilson Observatory, and Irwin has checked their survey and extended it to the Southern Hemisphere. Comparative studies of the color excesses for the very remote globular clusters in the direction of the galactic center and for the relatively nearby B stars in the same general direction, have shown that the strong interstellar absorption is concentrated in the outer rim of our Milky Way system, that is, in the region where the sun and earth are located. Even for the most transparent sections of the Milky Way in the direction of the galactic center, the indications are that two-thirds of the total observed obscuration occurs within 6000 light-years of our sun, leaving the remaining 20,000 or so light-years that separate us from the galactic center relatively free from cosmic dust.

How regular or irregular is the distribution of the interstellar dust in the general haze? Is it smooth or does the superposition of many single dust clouds produce the total effect that we observe? At present it is impossible to give a positive answer to these questions. There is apparently no region along the galactic circle where the view is perfectly clear. In a few places some galaxies shine through the haze in the galactic belt, but even there the number of faint galaxies is far below par and a total absorption of several magnitudes is indicated.

Because of the irregularities in the total distribution of the faint external galaxies (they are inclined to come in bunches too!) estimates of total absorptions from galaxy data for a given area may well be off by as much as half a magnitude. In spite of such uncertainties, the observed deficiencies in the numbers of faint galaxies can tell us much about the extent of some of the largest single clouds. The large dark nebulae in Orion and Taurus, Cepheus, and Ophiuchus are not only star-poor regions but they are also deficient in faint galaxies.

We should not underestimate the total effect of the isolated dark nebulae. Only the nearest of those nebulae will be discovered by an inspection of Milky Way photographs. The Coalsack is conspicuous to us because it is probably well within 500 light-years and covers a large angular field. But we should realize that it would hardly have been discovered if it had been ten times as far away, at 5000 light-years. Not only would it then cover only 1 percent of its present area, but it would further lack contrast because of the many foreground stars. Greenstein has computed that the known dark nebulae alone may account for 30 percent of the total haze for distances up to 3000 light-years.

In the late 1930's, a group of Soviet astronomers led by Ambartsumian introduced the hypothesis that the interstellar absorption may be produced entirely by chance agglomerations of small obscuring clouds, with average radii of the order of 25 light-years, with the average photographic absorption per cloud of the order of 0.2 magnitude and with the average line of sight intersecting about one cloud every 500 light-years. This attractive and picturesque arrangement of a cumulus-cloud-like structure for the interstellar haze received for a while strong support from groups of American and European astronomers, but it has not been verified in detail by subsequent analysis. Two types of observations speak against it. First, we notice that the known dark nebulae are by no means distributed at random; they tend to congregate in large complexes, such as the Taurus and Ophiuchus dark nebulosities. Second, we find for the large smooth stretches of the Milky Way, where there is little or no indication of structure, that space reddening is present all along the Milky Way and that nowhere is the total photographic absorption less than half a magnitude at 5000 light-years from the sun. And finally we should mention that nowhere have we found any clear "holes"—patches of clear sky between the cumuli—which should occur under the pure cloud hypothesis. The current trend is then to look upon the interstellar absorbing medium as a turbulent affair. As far as we can tell today, there is probably some continuous haze, but it seems as though the isolated dark dust clouds are responsible for more than half of the observed absorption and scattering. It seems likely that there is a large range in the sizes and average absorptions of the dark clouds, but as yet we cannot say anything definite about the distribution law of sizes.

*   *

*

Interstellar

Polarization   Every user of Polaroid glasses knows that light rays do not necessarily vibrate with equal intensity in all planes with different orientations relative to the line of sight. Polaroid glasses take most of the glare out of the sun's rays reflected by the road surface because they remove effectively the rays in the plane of vibration that is strongest in reflection. Effects of light polarization have been observed in the scattered light from the corona of our sun and in the atmosphere of planets, but until 1949 no one expected that the light of distant stars might become polarized as a result of its passage through the interstellar medium.

To produce interstellar polarization in the light of distant stars requires not only a preponderance of somewhat elongated particles in interstellar space, but, further, some powerful mechanism to align these particles over a very great distance. This, so it was reasoned, would not likely occur and it came therefore as a great surprise when, in 1949, Hall at the U. S. Naval Observatory and Hiltner at the McDonald Observatory announced simultaneously that they had succeeded in detecting marked polarization effects in the light of distant stars of our Milky Way system. The observations of Hall and Hiltner were made with photoelectric polarimeters, which are instruments that permit comparative measurements of any star's brightness in different planes of vibration. The recording by photoelectric means guarantees a remarkably high precision of measurement, which is essential when one deals with as small observed effects as those of interstellar polarization. Even in the most extreme case, the differences in intensity for the planes of greatest and of least intensity amount to no more than 0.15 magnitude and for the majority of even the distant reddened stars, the differences are less than 0.02 or 0.03 magnitude.

A sufficient variety of distant stars has now been observed so that we can say definitely that the polarization is produced by particles of interstellar space. Polarization affects the light of all distant stars along the belt of the Milky Way, irrespective of spectral class or absolute magnitude. Strong polarization effects are observed only on stars that are highly reddened by intervening cosmic dust, even though strong reddening is not necessarily accompanied by high percentage polarization. The fact that polarization and reddening generally do go together speaks strongly in favor of the hypothesis that polarization is associated with cosmic dust.

This conclusion is strengthened by the further remarkable observation that similar polarization characteristics are often found over fairly large sections of the Milky Way. In the direction of the constellation Perseus, for example, distant stars over a large area of the sky show comparable high degrees of polarization and a remarkably close alignment of their principal planes of polarization. Such phenomena can be understood only if one assumes that the polarization is produced by clouds or cloud complexes with dimensions of the order of several hundred light-years that are composed of interstellar particles with roughly parallel alignments. In some sections of the Milky Way the parallel alignment is very marked, whereas in others the planes of polarization present a more jumbled picture. This is shown very nicely in the diagram for the southern Milky Way prepared by Elske Smith from observations at the Boyden Station (Fig. 95). There appears to be a marked trend for the electric vector of the light to lie principally in the plane of the galaxy, the magnetic vector being oriented perpendicular to the plane. This indicates in all probability that the elongated particles that are responsible for producing the polarization effects are oriented preferably with their long axes at right angles to the plane of the Milky Way.

To produce detectable polarization effects in the light of distant stars requires first of all that there be in interstellar space somewhat elongated particles and, second, that some mechanism exist to align these particles in a more or less parallel fashion over very large regions. Precise calculations show that the required elongation for the particles need not be very great. Greenstein has shown that ellipsoidal or egg-shaped particles for which the ratio between the longest and shortest axes is 5 to 4 should satisfy the first requirement. The mystery is, however, just how these elongated particles are properly aligned in clouds of dimensions of some hundreds of light years. Several theories have been suggested to account for the alignment, but everyone has the uncomfortable, yet welcome, feeling that the last word on this matter has not yet been said.

Thus far the theories that·call for magnetic fields to produce the alignment seem to have received the most attention. Spitzer and Tukey have suggested that the polarization is produced by elongated metallic particles in interstellar clouds of very low temperature. They produce parallel alignment of the particles by a weak magnetic field, the strength of which in the terminology of the physicist should at least be equal to 0.0001 gauss. Davis and Greenstein have pointed out that it does not seem very likely that tiny metallic particles are present in abundance in interstellar clouds. In their theory the tiny ice particles, concerning which we spoke earlier in

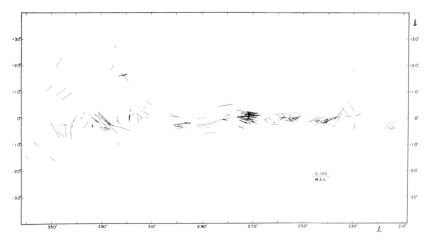

Fig. 95.   Interstellar polarization in the Southern Hemisphere. The distribution of the maximum electric vectors of the light of stars exhibiting polarization in the southern Milky Way. The galactic longitudes l and latitudes b are shown. The diagram covers the Milky Way from Puppis ($l = 210°$) through Carina ($l = 255°$), the Southern Coalsack ($l = 270°$), to Scorpius and Sagittarius ($l = 310°$ to $340°$). (From data by Elske v. P. Smith based on observations at Boyden Station.)

the chapter, are supposed to be elongated and spinning rapidly and they are further supposed to have a 10-percent admixture of metals. The Davis and Greenstein theory requires magnetic fields of only 0.00001 gauss and the rapid spinning of the magnetized particles can apparently produce sufficient alignment for polarization even at temperatures for the interstellar clouds that are considerably higher than those assumed by Spitzer and Tukey.

At the present time the Davis and Greenstein theory seems to be meeting with fairly general approval, but we should mention briefly that there are rival hypotheses, especially those of Gold and Zirin, in which it is supposed that the alignment of the particles may be produced by streaming effects in the interstellar gas. A few years ago theories that did not call for the presence of fairly strong galactic magnetic fields had considerable appeal since astrophysicists found it difficult to imagine that such fields could exist in the vast spaces between the stars. Gradually other types of indirect evidence for the presence of such magnetic fields have appeared, notably the

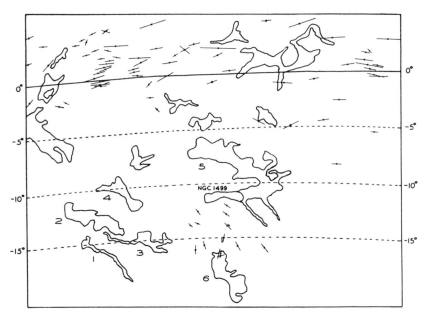

Fig. 96.   Relation between dark nebulosities and polarization. Shajn calls attention to the tendency for long filamentary structures in emission nebulae and in dark clouds to lie parallel to the galactic equator. This figure shows a region in Perseus-Taurus with dark nebulosities. The short lines indicate the direction of the interstellar magnetic lines of force as deduced from the observations of the polarization of light for distant stars made by Hiltner and Hall.

suggestion that these magnetic fields may play an important role in arranging the gas clouds of our own and other galaxies in the familiar spiral patterns and that they may help to account for the tremendous energies of the cosmic rays. Today we are rather inclined to look with favor upon theories that require interstellar magnetic fields to produce alignment, be it of the tiny interstellar particles or of the enormous gas clouds of our galaxy.

One of the most remarkable phenomena suggesting the presence of large-scale magnetic fields is the alignment of wisps of dark and bright nebulosity for rather large sections of the Milky Way; Shajn and Rouscol have especially drawn attention to this phenomenon. Shajn has derived for some sections the direction of the magnetic field that he holds responsible for the observed elongations of the dark nebulae features; he finds that the orientation of this magnetic field agrees within permissible limits of error with that derived from the observed polarization effects for stars seen through these nebulae.

It should not be thought that polarization effects are limited to cosmic dust features. Shklovsky predicted from theory that strong polarization effects might be expected from very fast moving electrons in magnetic fields of interstellar space. Dombrovsky observed the effect in the Crab Nebula (Fig. 103); his measures have been confirmed and extended by Oort and by Walraven, who find almost complete polarization in certain parts of the Crab Nebula. Baade has made some very high-resolution photographs of the inner filamentary structure of the Crab Nebula and he finds filaments with diameters of the order of 1 to 3 seconds of arc that show 100-percent polarization.

8

Radio Astronomy
and The Milky Way

During the second half of the nineteenth century astronomy was revolutionized by the introduction of spectroscopy and photography. It may well be that future generations will remember the middle of the twentieth century as the time when radio astronomy brought about a new revolution. Spectroscopy and photography together brought a wholly new approach to the study of the Milky Way system and the present volume bears witness to the powerful effects that these new tools had upon the advance of our science. Radio astronomy provides the tool for exploration into a completely new section of the electromagnetic spectrum.

All too often people forget that our knowledge of the visible and photographable universe depends on studies over a relatively small range of wavelength. The most used part of the electromagnetic spectrum, at least as far as Milky Way research is concerned, lies between wavelengths 3000 and 9000 angstroms. Research at shorter

193

wavelengths can at present be done only from rockets under conditions that are about as far from ideal as one could imagine; our sun is the only celestial body for which it has been possible to record radiation in the wavelength interval between 1000 and 3000 angstroms. The atmosphere of the earth is still a very effective curtain for the ultraviolet and for shorter wavelengths. We shall have to await the putting into operation of the first space platform before the ultraviolet and x-ray spectra of the stars and nebulae of the Milky Way will become accessible to the astronomer. In the infrared part of the spectrum 9000 angstroms represents about the greatest wavelength used thus far in survey work of the Milky Way system. There have been a few isolated instances in which research has been carried out at greater wavelengths, notably by photoelectric and thermocouple techniques, and the Eastman Kodak Company is making great strides in the development of more sensitive emulsions for wavelengths between 9000 and 12,000 angstroms. We are therefore most generous if we say that the wavelength interval between 1000 and 30,000 angstroms is now accessible to the astronomer. Since 1 angstrom is only $1/10^8$ (0.000,000,01) centimeter, the extreme accessible range of wavelength in centimeters is from 0.00001 centimeter to 0.00030 centimeter. This extreme range represents only between four and five octaves of the electromagnetic spectrum. To this narrow traditional spectrum window opening on our universe we now add the new and much broader radio window.

The accessible part of the radio spectrum falls between about 0.5 centimeter wavelength and 25 to 30 meters. On the short-wavelength side, molecular absorption in the earth's atmosphere stops the radiation that comes from beyond our atmosphere very much as molecular absorption hinders our visual observations between 0.0001 and 0.0003 centimeters (Fig. 97). For wavelengths above 30 meters, reflection by the electrically charged high layer of our atmosphere, the ionosphere, makes it impossible for radio waves from outer space to penetrate to the surface of the earth. But, fortunately, we have a relatively clear radio window in the range between molecular absorption and ionospheric reflection. The range of transmitted wavelengths is considerably larger in the radio spectrum than in the visible and photographic spectrum. Expressed in octaves, we find that the radio window permits the free transmission of between 11 and 12 octaves, as contrasted with the meager 4 to 5 octaves of the normal spectral range.

Radio astronomy was born in 1931–32 when Jansky, of the Bell Telephone Laboratories, discovered extraterrestrial radio noise at a wavelength of 14.7 meters, which came in strongest from the direction of the center of our Milky Way system. Astronomers expressed great interest in Jansky's discovery, but they did little to promote further research on the subject. In the late 1930's Grote Reber, an electronic engineer of Wheaton, Illinois, undertook the first large-scale study of radio radiation from the Milky Way, but the coming of World War II effectively stopped research in the field. Out of the war years, however, came the development of radar and of many new techniques of value for research in radio astronomy. Since the middle 1940's, radio astronomy has taken wings. Australia, Great Britain, and Holland have produced the bulk of the research on which we are reporting here, but research workers in other countries—notably the United States and Canada—have in recent years made important contributions to the young science.

In the optical region we distinguish between three sorts of spectra: continuous, absorption, and emission. In a continuous spectrum all wavelengths are represented and the intensity distribution throughout the spectrum depends mostly on the temperature of the source responsible for its emission. In the laboratory, a glowing solid produces a continuous spectrum, and the same sort of spectrum is produced in the lower layers of a star's atmosphere, that is, in its photosphere. In an absorption spectrum, relatively dark absorption lines are seen projected against the continuum. The spectra of the majority of the stars are of this variety. The absorption lines are produced by atoms and molecules in the star's upper atmosphere. Then there are the emission spectra, which, in their purest forms,

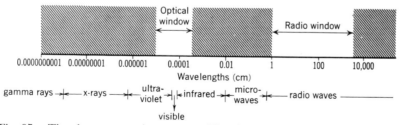

Fig. 97. The electromagnetic spectrum. The electromagnetic spectrum extends from the very short wavelengths of the gamma rays through the x-rays, the ultra-violet, and the photographic and visible spectrum into the infrared, the micro waves, and the long radio waves. In the optical range we have now accessible the interval between 1,000 and 30,000 angstroms (0.00001 cm to 0.0003 cm). The radio window extends from about 1 cm to 25 or 30 meters.

are observed in the majority of diffuse nebulae and in planetary nebulae. In the radio range of wavelengths we were at first almost entirely concerned with continuous spectra. The background radiation from the Milky Way is continuous and so is the radiation received from the point sources. To date, there is on record only one instance in which an emission line has been observed, the 21-centimeter line of neutral hydrogen; only in a few exceptional cases has the 21-centimeter line been observed in absorption. Soviet radio astronomers have reported observations of one additional absorption line, a line near wavelength 92 centimeters observed in the direction of the galactic center and attributed to the deuterium atom. Instrumental difficulties render this result still very uncertain.

We shall deal first with the continuous radio radiation from our galaxy and beyond, discussing separately, as far as possible, the background radiation from our galaxy and the radio radiation from discrete sources. The discussion of the 21-centimeter radiation will be reserved for the concluding section of the chapter.

*   *

*

Continuous Background Radiation from the Galaxy

Following Jansky's discovery of radio radiation from the Milky Way (1931), the first large-scale and accurate survey was completed by Reber (1944), who used a 31-foot paraboloid with recording equipment operating at a wavelength of 185 centimeters. To Grote Reber, more than to anyone else, belongs the credit for having started the new science of radio astronomy of the Milky Way. He began his work at his home in Wheaton, Illinois and later moved to the National Bureau of Standards in Washington, D. C. He has lately continued his researches in Hawaii and New Zealand.

Reber realized that, to have any resolving power at all at wavelengths of a few meters, a large paraboloid reflector would be required. It is well known that the angular resolving power of a reflector depends on the ratio between the wavelength of the light analyzed and the aperture of the reflector. Since the wavelengths of visible and photographic light are between 0.0001 and 0.00001 centimeter, a mirror such as that of the 200-inch Hale reflector at Mount Palomar has a high resolving power of a few hundredths of a second of arc. But in Reber's case, the full 31-foot aperture of his mirror is only about six times the wavelength of the radiation that he was

investigating. It is therefore not surprising that the resolving power
of Reber's apparatus is only of the order of 12 degrees, so that at
best he could obtain no more than a diffuse, "washed out" picture
of the distribution over the sky of radiation with a wavelength of
185 centimeters (Fig. 98). The resolving power of Reber's survey
was, however, sufficient to show the principal features of interest
for Milky Way research. Radio radiation is to some extent present
all over the sky, but it shows a very marked concentration to the
belt of the Milky Way. Reber found regions of enhanced radio
emission in Cygnus and in Cassiopeia, but by far the strongest
radiation came from the general direction of the galactic center.

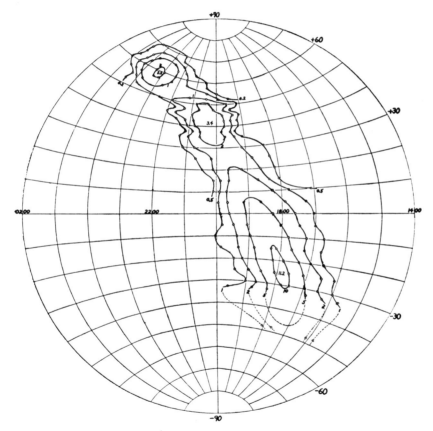

Fig. 98.   Reber's survey of 1944. Lines of equal intensity of galactic radio radiation at a wavelength of 185 cm recorded by Reber with his 31.4-foot parabolic
antenna. The strong radiation near $18^h - 25°$ comes from the direction of the
galactic center. The effect of the Cassiopeia discrete source, near 60°, and of the
sources in Cygnus, near 40°, can be seen in this early diagram.

Fig. 99. The helical antenna array of Ohio State University. This large antenna array has been used by Kraus and associates for the preparation of a sky map of radio radiation at a frequency of 250 megacycles per second.

Since Reber's research of 1944, several other accurate surveys have been completed and analyzed. Reber made a second survey (1948) at a wavelength of 62 centimeters and obtained results in agreement with his earlier survey, with the additional information that the strong radiation in Cygnus seemed to come from two centers. In Great Britain, Hey, Parsons, and Phillips in 1947 made a survey at a wavelength of 4.7 meters and one of the most recent American surveys is that made by Kraus of Ohio State University at a wavelength of 120 centimeters. To date, the most extensive research has been done at the Radio Physics Laboratory in Australia, where Bolton and Westfold published in 1950 the results of an accurate survey at a wavelength of 3 meters. The results of still other Australian surveys have been published by Allen and Gum and by Piddington and Minnett.

The common result of all surveys appears to be that the regions of equal intensity of radio radiation are arranged roughly symmetrically with respect to the equator of the Milky Way. The width of the Milky Way, as shown on the radio contour charts, is greater at long that at short wavelengths, but this may be in part an effect of lack of resolving power at longer wavelengths. Until the giant 250-foot steerable radio telescope is completed at Jodrell Bank near Manchester, England, one would therefore be inclined to place most weight on the available surveys at shorter wavelengths, but unfortunately the intensity of the radiation at these shorter wavelengths is so low that one can detect the radiation from only the brightest Milky Way regions. All surveys show that the radiation with maximum intensity reaches us from the direction of the Milky

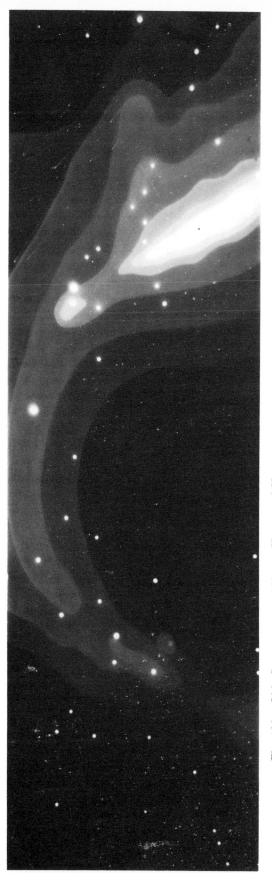

Fig. 100. Ohio State survey at 120 cm. Kraus and Ko at Ohio State University have surveyed the sky within reach from Columbus, Ohio, with the aid of the antenna array shown in Fig. 99. The contour lines represent lines of equal radio surface brightness. The beam width of the apparatus measures 1° in right ascension by 8° in declination.

Fig. 101.   The Australian 36-foot paraboloid. This instrument, which is movable only in altitude and which has therefore been used only for meridian transits, was employed by the radio astronomers at Sydney for the discovery of 21-cm radiation from the Large and Small Magellanic Clouds.

Way center in Sagittarius. The radio results indicate that the position of the galactic center is in a direction somewhere between galactic longitude 325° and 329°, galactic latitude 1° or 2° south of the galactic plane; Kraus places the direction to the center at $l = 327°8\,1$, $b = -1°4$. This position for the direction toward the galactic center is in full agreement with that obtained from studies of the distribution over the sky of globular clusters, novae, and cluster-type variables, as well as from studies of galactic rotation. It is also interesting to note that Seeger, Northcott, and Williamson find that the position of the galactic pole, as derived from their own and Reber's surveys, agrees well with determinations of the position of the galactic pole from optical data.

In discussions of the physics of stellar atmospheres, the distribution of brightness with wavelength in the continuous spectrum plays a very important role. From this brightness distribution, we derive for stars that are not appreciably affected by space reddening the probable temperatures of their atmospheres. In the same way, we might expect to learn something basic about the source or sources of the continuous radio radiation from studies of the distribution of intensity with wavelength in the radio continuum. This expectation has, alas, not yet been fulfilled, for we do not yet understand how the background radiation originates, at least not for the longer wavelengths. Let us start by describing briefly the basic observational data.

For wavelengths between 1 centimeter and 30–40 centimeters, the background radiation is very weak and it has only recently become possible to measure it with any degree of precision. The measured amounts are what one would expect from the radiation produced by passages of free electrons through the electric fields of protons. Hagen, Haddock, and their associates at the Naval Research Laboratory in Washington have measured the background radiation in the radio continuum at wavelengths of 3, 10, and 21 centimeters. They find strong radiations at these wavelengths coming to us from the direction of most of the familiar emission nebulae, such as the Orion Nebula, Messier 8, and the Trifid Nebula. Their researches prove conclusively that clouds of ionized gas—presumably mostly ionized hydrogen—produce measurable radio radiations at these wavelengths. The observed intensities at these wavelengths agree with those predicted by Greenstein for the temperatures in these nebulae. The principal puzzle that remains is why these radiations should be so strong for the general direction of the center of our galaxy, since we do not generally associate large amounts of ionized hydrogen with the nuclear regions of galaxies. Most probably the strong emission does not come from the center itself but rather from diffuse nebulae at distances of the order of 3000 parsecs from the sun in the direction of the center.

Real difficulties of interpretation arise when we turn to wavelengths of 50 centimeters and greater. Henyey and Keenan, as well as Townes, showed some years ago that one can explain the observed intensity of the background radiation as originating in the interstellar gas only if one assumes electron temperatures of the order of 100,000°. It is difficult to see how one could possibly justify prevailing electron temperatures of this order, since these should produce readily observable spectral effects in the optical range. The recent trend has therefore been to look elsewhere than in the interstellar gas for the origin of the observed strong radio radiation in the meter range of wavelengths.

The background radiation in the meter range does not show anywhere nearly as marked a concentration to the galactic circle as does the interstellar gas, and this is one additional reason why this radiation probably does not originate in the interstellar gas. In more general terms, the surface distribution over the sky as observed for the background radiation does not resemble the sort of distribution one would expect for radiation originating from sources associated with Population I; it looks more like a Population II distribution.

Unsöld was the first to suggest that the radio radiation in the meter range might not originate in the gas clouds of interstellar space, but rather that it is produced by the combined radiation from many unresolved point sources, or discrete sources. On the basis of the demonstrated small galactic concentration of the radio radiation, and the high concentration to the center of our galaxy, Unsöld suggested that the discrete sources are distributed like Population II objects. This theory has been redrawn in modified form by Westerhout and Oort of Leiden. They find that the observed intensity distribution over the sky as observed by Bolton and Westfold may be understood if we assume that the continuous background radiation observed at 3 meters is the result of contributions from thousands of faint point sources distributed throughout the Milky Way very much in the fashion of the unglamorous G and K dwarfs. This assumption represents a fine first step, but since we have no evidence regarding the way in which the point sources operate—or just what they are—we have no start on a final theory.

There is one additional puzzling phenomenon, first clearly noted by Westerhout and Oort and since confirmed by Wyatt: after we account for the maximum contribution from our Milky Way system to the general galactic radio radiation, there remains an unaccounted-for component that is constant all over the sky. For the wavelength of the survey of Bolton and Westfold, Westerhout and Oort estimate this residual radiation as equivalent in intensity to what would be produced by a uniform background temperature of the sky of 600° Kelvin at a wavelength of 3 meters. It seems most likely that this radiation represents the total contribution from the background of faint galaxies beyond our Milky Way system.

One relatively recent bit of observational evidence for the Andromeda Nebula (Messier 31) may have considerable bearing on the interpretation of the observed background component. Baldwin at the Cavendish Laboratory has observed radiation at 3.7 meters wavelength, which appears to originate in a spherical halo or "corona" of the spiral in Andromeda. Why should not our own galaxy be enveloped similarly? If our galaxy should have its own radio corona, then it would presumably account for a large fraction of the uniform background.

*   *

*

Discrete Radio Sources

The discovery of *discrete radio sources*—in the past often referred to as point sources or radio stars—represents one of the most startling developments of our times. Offhand it might seem an almost hopeless task to locate and study radio sources of limited angular dimensions and distinguish them from the relatively smooth background radiation. The average present-day radio telescope presents us with a very blurred and washed-out picture of the radio sky and it would take a paraboloid radio mirror with an aperture of a mile or so to prove the presence of a discrete source with a diameter of 2 or 3 minutes of arc. It has, however, already proved possible by ingenious applications of interferometer techniques to locate and study intense point sources of such diameters.

In 1946 Hey, Parsons, and Phillips first obtained the remarkable result that the intensity of the continuous radiation in Cygnus was subject to fluctuations with periods of only a few minutes. It has since been shown that these fluctuations were probably not intrinsic fluctuations in the source, but rather that they were produced when the radiation passed through the upper layers of our ionosphere. But the 1946 observations did succeed in hastening the search for point sources of radio radiation, or at least sources of small angular dimensions. Pawsey at the Radio Physics Laboratory in Australia suggested certain experiments with interference techniques and in 1948 Bolton and Stanley succeeded in proving that the source of the strong radio radiation at a wavelength of 3 meters in Cygnus possesses an angular diameter of not more than 8 minutes of arc. More recent work has shown that this early estimate for the dimensions was somewhat too large and the chances are that the source is no bigger than 3 minutes by 1 minute of arc. Since 1948, interferometer research has been carried on on a large scale not only by the Australian radio physicists, but also in England, especially by Ryle and Smith, and by Hanbury Brown and associates. About 200 of these discrete sources of radio radiation have thus far been located with certainty and most of these have already been verified independently; the total list of suspected sources has as many as 2000 entries. The strong sources show a rather marked concentration to the band of the Milky Way, whereas the fainter ones are distributed more uniformly over the sky.

Two varieties of interferometers have thus far been developed for purposes of research in radio astronomy. The first of these is the sea interferometer, the second the meridian interferometer. In the sea interferometer of Bolton and Stanley (Fig. 102) we observe a source after it has just risen above the horizon. When the source is only a few degrees above the horizon, the radio antenna receives radiation from the source directly and also radiation reflected by the surface of the ocean. There is obviously a path difference between the direct and reflected rays, the reflected ray having traversed the longer path. The antenna is mounted on a high cliff facing the point of the horizon where the source has just risen. If the two paths differ by a whole number of wavelengths and if the source is strictly a point source, then the tops of the waves from the direct ray and the tops of the waves from the reflected ray will arrive at the same time and they should simply strengthen one another. But when the difference between the two paths is 0.5, 1.5,

2.5, . . . wavelengths, then the tops of the direct waves will arrive simultaneously with the bottoms of the reflected waves, thus canceling one another, and the minima of the direct waves will arrive at the same time as the maxima of the reflected waves, again yielding zero intensity. This is the well-known phenomenon of interference.

What will happen if the source is not strictly a point source but has a finite angular dimension? At the moment when the path difference between the direct and reflected rays equals an odd number of half wavelengths for one point in the source (thus producing perfect interference and zero intensity for the radiation reaching us from that particular point in the source), the path difference for another point in the extended source will not be the same and perfect interference will not take place. An extended source will therefore never produce really zero intensity; we may even estimate the angular size of the source from the ratio of intensities of maximum and minimum reflections. The greatest advantage of the sea interferometer is that the time of rising of the source is very clearly marked and this permits an accurate determination of its position. The greatest disadvantage is that the critical observations are made at the moment when the source is rising, which is also the moment when the slanting path of the radiation through the ionosphere of

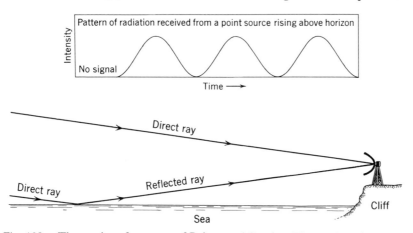

Fig. 102.   The sea interferometer of Bolton and Stanley. The sea interferometer combines the radiation received directly from a point source with the radiation reflected from the sea. When the difference of path length is equal to a whole number of wavelengths, favorable interference occurs and the signal will be strengthened. Unfavorable interference and hence cancellation of the signal will occur if the path lengths differ by ½, 1½, 2½, . . . wavelengths.

the earth is longest and when refraction effects and other ionospheric disturbances are maximum.

In the meridian interferometer, one makes use of two antennas, aligned along a north-south line and separated by a known number of wavelengths of the radiation that is being recorded. As the source approaches the meridian, the path difference between the rays to the two antennas will alternately be a whole number of wavelengths, which produces enhanced intensity as received, or an odd number of half wavelengths, which produces perfect interference and hence zero intensity for the two waves. An alternating pattern of maximum and minimum intensity is thus produced. For a strictly point source the intensity in the minima should go down to zero, but an extended source will yield some residual intensity at minimum. From the ratio between maximum and minimum intensity, the angular extent of the source may again be determined.

In the past few years, several modifications of the meridian interferometer have been designed and built. Mills and Bolton of Australia, Smith of Cambridge, England, and Hanbury Brown of Manchester, England, have all put into operation equipment designed to measure accurately the positions and angular dimensions of the discrete radio sources. The Cygnus source appears to be the smallest of the strong sources, with dimensions, as we have already indicated, of 1 minute by 3 minutes of arc. Other discrete sources appear to be considerably larger, with diameters of the order of at least 0.5° indicated for relatively strong sources in Sagittarius and in Vela. Bolton's research suggests that there may be many sources with diameters of the order of a few degrees.

The discrete sources are not in any way related to the brighter stars. A hypothetical observer with eyesight sensitive to radio radiation in the meter range would "see" a Milky Way in his sky with the direction of the center in Sagittarius shining with the greatest intensity. If his eyes were to provide him with high resolution, there would also be in his picture a number of bright sources, some of them apparently starlike and others with angular dimensions comparable to those of the moon or larger. But the pattern of the constellations formed by the discrete radio sources would bear no resemblance whatsoever to our familiar constellations of the night sky.

In recent years much time and effort have been spent on the identification of at least some of the point sources with known objects observed visually or photographically. It is not surprising that the nearby bright galaxies show up as discrete sources. One of the first important successes of the Jodrell Bank 220-foot fixed antenna was the identification by Hanbury Brown of a faint radio source identical in position with the Andromeda Nebula. Others among the great nearby galaxies—Messier 33, Messier 51, and Messier 101—have been identified with radio sources. It is rather to be expected that all of the nearer galaxies will prove to be at least faint discrete sources in the radio range of wavelength, since it is likely that most galaxies would have radio sources of the same variety as are so prominently present in our galaxy. We realize at the same time that identification of a discrete source at radio wavelength with a nearby galaxy proves only that the other galaxy has its own radio sources and we learn nothing about their true nature. Of more interest, therefore, are the identifications of radio sources with known objects in our own galaxy.

The first major identification of a discrete source with a known celestial object was made by Bolton and Stanley, who showed that the third brightest discrete source coincides in position precisely with the famous Crab Nebula (Fig. 103). This identification may be considered a definite one. It has long been known that the Crab Nebula represents the aftereffects of a supernova explosion which presumably took place in A.D. 1054. Photographs in the light of the

Fig. 103.   The Crab Nebula in Taurus, the result of a supernova explosion of A.D. 1054. It marks the position of the third most powerful discrete radio source. (200-inch Hale-Palomar photograph.)

hydrogen Hα line by Baade and Minkowski show a remarkably fine filamentary structure for the gas that appears to be responsible for the hydrogen emission. Here we seem to have the first important clue to an understanding of the discrete sources: the radio emission seems to originate in or near a region where ionized gases are in highly turbulent motion. We still lack a satisfactory theory of just why turbulent gas motions should produce strong radio emissions, but the observations seem to suggest that they do.

A study of the possible optical objects that are identical with the stronger discrete radio sources has been made by Minkowski and Baade with the aid of the Palomar telescopes. In the position of the strong radio source in Cygnus, the Palomar photographs show as the only remarkable features two faint galaxies apparently in collision. This identification suggests that collisions between the gas clouds of the two galaxies produce in some as yet not understood fashion turbulent streaming which in turn produces the observed radio radiation. Here the puzzle as to the nature of the process at work is heightened by the fact that the estimated distance from the sun to the pair of galaxies in collision is 200,000,000 light-years, according to the best available estimates. The strongest discrete radio source is observed in Cassiopeia. Minkowski has made special studies of the faint emission nebulosity that is apparently responsible for the radiation. This nebulosity, which is apparently located in the Perseus spiral arm of our galaxy, has on photographs a most unusual appearance, almost like scratches on the emulsion. Spectral studies by Minkowski show it to be composed of very turbulent gas masses with velocities running into the thousands of kilometers per second. This same variety of turbulent emission nebulosity is found at the positions of some other sources, notably the discrete sources of finite radio size in Puppis and Vela.

The discrete radio sources are not all of the same kind. We have already noted the marked differences in angular dimensions, which suggest true differences in linear dimensions. Also, it has been found that the energy distribution with wavelength in the radio spectrum is not identical for all sources. Most sources emit much more energy at long than at short wavelengths, but the Taurus source (identified with the Crab Nebula) shows a more even distribution of energy with wavelength. We must consider as a class apart the discrete sources discovered by Hagen, Haddock, and others at short wavelengths and identified with known optical emission nebulae; they

Fig. 104.   The Australian Mills cross. Bernard Mills and his group at Sydney have constructed the very large array shown here as a search instrument with a narrow beam for the study of discrete radio sources.

radiate in the centimeter and decimeter range by the process of free-free transitions, that is, by a simple atomic process in which radiation in the radio range is produced as a consequence of the encounter of protons and free electrons.

In the past few years, research on discrete radio sources has developed in an almost unbelievable fashion. Ryle and his associates at the Cavendish Laboratory have built a beautiful interferometer array. It consists of four major components, each 600 feet in length and spaced in pairs 2000 feet apart in an east-west direction and

400 feet apart in a north-south direction. With this apparatus Ryle has already completed a radio sky "map" that has 1936 sources plotted on it. Mills is solving the problem of mapping in a different fashion through the use of a "Mills cross" (Fig. 104), an antenna array that produces a single narrow pencillike beam and is constructed especially to search for and study faint discrete sources; his first list contains over 1000 sources and it covers only a narrow belt of the sky.

We may as well accept the fact that the path of identification of discrete radio sources with optical objects is going to be a thorny one! First, we note that the two brightest radio sources, the ones in Cygnus and in Cassiopeia, were identified with difficulty and that they were found to coincide with very inconspicuous optical phenomena. If these had been among the weaker of the 1936 sources on Ryle's list, the optical identification would have been very difficult and uncertain, if for no other reason than that the radio positions must be known with high precision before identification can be attempted. Then there is at present considerable confusion because the positions of the fainter objects observed at different radio observatories do not always check—confusion that arises in part because of effects produced by the bothersome side lobes of the instrumental patterns of the radio equipment. The Ryle and the Mills lists have only very few objects in common and no significant progress is being made in the identification of new sources. To overcome these difficulties, we should in the future pay much attention to high precision in the measurement of positions and we must stress the importance of multiple checks with equipment of widely different design.

The
21-Centimeter
Line of Neutral
Hydrogen

*   *

*

We have thus far dealt wholly with radio radiation constituting a continuous spectrum. We now turn our attention to an emission line in the microwave region, the line produced by neutral interstellar hydrogen. On several occasions we have already referred to the optical spectrum of neutral hydrogen, notably in Chapter 6 in our discussion of the physics of the interstellar gas. The neutral hydrogen atom possesses a definite series of discrete energy levels and the known lines of the Lyman, Balmer, Paschen, and other spectral series of the neutral hydrogen atom are produced by transitions or "jumps" from one energy level to another. Since the early days of the quantum theory of atomic spectra, it was known that some of the energy levels of the neutral hydrogen atom were multiple ones, thus suggesting the so-called "fine structure" for these particular levels. But the lowest level of the neutral hydrogen atom, the Lyman level, did not possess this fine structure. In later years, however, physicists were able to show that the hydrogen atom possesses a "hyperfine structure," which was determined by differences in orientation of the magnetic spin of the outer electron and the corresponding magnetic spin of the nucleus. The Lyman level of neutral hydrogen is found to be really a pair of levels with a small energy difference, depending upon whether the orientations of the spins of the nucleus and the electron are parallel or oppositely directed; the level corresponding to parallel spins has the slightly greater energy. The energy difference between the two hyperfine Lyman levels corresponds to a wavelength of 21 centimeters, or a frequency of 1420 megacycles per second. The upper of the two hyperfine levels is, however, a metastable one, which means that transitions from the upper to the lower level will only very rarely occur spontaneously. Precise calculations show that such spontaneous transitions take place on the average only once in 11,000,000 years for a single atom in the higher of the two hyperfine levels.

Because of the low transition probability between the upper and lower hyperfine Lyman levels, the prospects of observing the 21-centimeter line from interstellar space did not seem very promising. But in 1944, van de Hulst of Leiden suggested that the situation might not be as bleak as it seemed and that the vast supply of interstellar hydrogen might suffice to produce an observable line in spite of the small probability that a transition would take place. Also, it should be remembered that the mean lifetime of 11,000,000 years applies to a totally undisturbed hydrogen atom. The hydrogen atoms of interstellar space are left reasonably well alone, but once in every 300 years or so any particular atom will collide with one of its neighbors and these collisions might help to speed up the frequency of transitions between the two hyperfine levels. Van de Hulst's suggestion made a sufficient impression on Dutch astronomers and radio engineers that it was decided to build in Holland special apparatus for the detection and the study of the 21-centimeter line. Independently, similar work was undertaken by Ewen

and Purcell, Harvard University physicists, and they were the first
to produce proof that the interstellar hydrogen line was observable.
Ewen and Purcell announced their discovery on March 25, 1951,
and within six weeks Oort and Muller from Holland confirmed the
discovery. Very shortly afterwards, the 21-centimeter line was also
observed by Christiansen and Hindman of the Radio Physics Laboratory in Sidney, Australia.

If all the hydrogen gas in our galactic system were at rest, the
observed line at a wavelength of 21 centimeter would be very sharp
and narrow. Turbulent motions in the hydrogen clouds produce,
through the Doppler effect, a slight spread in the wavelengths that
are received and this range of wavelengths is further increased
through the Doppler shifts produced by the rotation of our galaxy.
The observed radiation from a given direction of the sky is therefore spread over a considerable range of wavelength. In many directions the width of the line, with its normal very sharp frequency
of 1420 megacycles per second, is somewhat greater than 1 mega-
cycle per second.

The galactic 21-centimeter radiation is so weak that it requires
special techniques for its detection. To record the weak radiations
directly would not only require extremely sensitive apparatus, but
also perfect stability of amplification for the received signal. The
method of recording these faint signals is that suggested by Dicke,
who developed in 1946 a simple method for measuring directly by
electronic means the difference in intensity between the received
signal and a standard source. In the case of the 21-centimeter radiation, one records the difference in intensity between the radiation
received at a given wavelength inside the line and the intensity at
a nearby wavelength in the continuum outside the line. One refers
to the wavelength interval measured within the line as the *signal
band,* and to that outside the line in the continuum as the *comparison
band.* Each measurement consists in recording the difference between the intensity of the radiation from the signal band and that
of the radiation from the comparison band. The difference in wavelength between the signal band and the center of the comparison
band is kept constant and the complete measurement of a line profile consists of a continuous measurement starting at one edge of the
observed profile, passing through the central portion of the line, and
continuing to the other edge of the line profile. To smooth out as
far as possible random fluctuations in the recorded currents, one

makes the filter-pass band for the comparison signal as broad as possible and proceeds slowly along the line, using conveniently long integrating times at each wavelength.

The line profile in Fig. 105 has been obtained with the 24-foot radio telescope of the Agassiz Station (Fig. 106). The horizontal scale is one of frequency (or wavelength) and to each measured frequency there corresponds a certain radial velocity of approach (negative) or recession (positive) of the emitting source. The measured intensities are indicated on the vertical scale. The pair of profiles shown are successive scans for the same center in the sky, one with the frequency at which we are recording slowly increasing during the scan, the other with the frequency gradually decreasing. The equipment permits at all times the precise determination of the frequency for which the intensity of the radiation is being measured.

We can thus obtain profiles of the 21-centimeter line for any chosen direction in space and one naturally asks what information may be obtained from an analysis of these profiles. Let us, for simplicity, suppose first that we are observing in a direction so selected

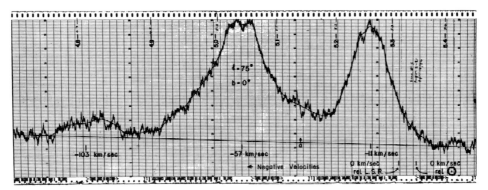

Fig. 105. A 21-cm profile. The profile was traced by Matthews with the 24-foot Agassiz Station radio telescope for a position in the sky at galactic longitude $l = 75°$, latitude $b = 0°$. The horizontal scale measures the precise wavelength, and the vertical scale the intensity of the radiation received at that wavelength. Since the radiation originates entirely from neutral hydrogen atoms, all emitting at the same wavelength when at rest, any observed shift in wavelength from the standard value must be due to radial velocity of approach ($-$) or recession ($+$) of the emitting cloud of atoms. The radial velocities, here mostly of approach, are shown marked on the horizontal scale. The marked velocities are relative to pure circular galactic rotation at the sun (L. S. R. = local standard of rest); the shifted zero of radial velocities relative to the sun is also shown. Note the presence of three major maxima near velocities of approach of 11, 57, and 103 km/sec, which correspond to intersections between the line of sight and the Orion, Perseus, and Distant spiral arms.

Fig. 106. The 24-foot radio telescope at Agassiz Station. The radio telescope shown here has a steerable paraboloid antenna of expanded aluminum mesh, which concentrates the radio radiation received upon a dipole feed located at the end of the long pole reaching to the focus. The radiation is then recorded in the building underneath the telescope. The mounting is of equatorial design and permits accurate following of any given radio source over a period of several hours. (Photograph by Walter R. Fleischer.)

that the interstellar clouds of hydrogen along the entire observed line of sight are without exception neither approaching nor receding from us. Simple calculations by Purcell and Oort, since confirmed by observation, show that in the galactic plane we can probably not "see" to distances much greater than about 5000 light-years. The self-absorption in a hydrogen cloud 5000 light-years in depth and containing on the average one neutral hydrogen atom per cubic centimeter will be so great that 21-centimeter quanta emitted by atoms beyond 5000 light-years will have little chance of reaching the sun and earth without being reabsorbed on the way. In spite of the extreme weakness of the 21-centimeter radiation, there would then be sufficient hydrogen along the line of sight to produce an optically "thick" layer, a fog thick enough that we cannot penetrate it. In such a thick fog the central intensity in the line is determined by the temperature of the interstellar hydrogen, which, for the H(I) regions in which the 21-centimeter line is produced, appears to be close to 60° Kelvin (see Chapter 6). For a really thick fog, it has been shown by Wild and by Heeschen that the observed line profile should be flat topped; the width of the observed line should depend only on the average random velocity of the neutral hydrogen clouds along the line of sight, which has been estimated to be of the order of 8 kilometers per second. Line profiles of the described varieties might be observed for the general direction of the center of our galaxy and the direction exactly opposite to it.

The situation becomes totally different when one considers observation along a line of sight for which radial velocity shifts do occur. We have already discussed in Chapter 5 the rotation of our galaxy and it is evident that the assumption of the absence of systematic radial velocity shifts along the line of sight will hold only for the direction of the galactic center and the anticenter—all this on the assumption that the hydrogen in the galaxy does indeed rotate as required by the Oort-Lindblad theory, that is, in circular orbits. We showed in Chapter 5 that zero radial velocity from galactic rotation could be expected near the sun also for galactic longitudes differing by 90° from those of the galactic center and anticenter, but it can readily be seen that this conclusion will not be valid once we reach to distances of 6000 light-years or greater; observations have demonstrated already that in the study of the 21-centimeter radiation we must from the start keep in mind that we are concerned with radiation reaching us from very great distances in our Milky Way system.

Oort, van de Hulst, and Muller have made to date the most complete study of 21-centimeter profiles along the Milky Way. We reproduce their chart of profiles in Fig. 107. Since we know that hydrogen is commonly associated with spiral arms in galaxies outside our own and probably in our own galaxy also, we may surmise that the maxima of intensity in the 21-centimeter profiles are caused by clouds of neutral hydrogen associated with the spiral arms of our own galaxy. If we could only find some way of estimating the distances of the clouds that produce the various maxima, we should obtain an outline of the remote spiral structure of our own galaxy. At the present time there is at least one way in which we may estimate roughly the distance of the cloud corresponding to any particular intensity peak in the 21-centimeter profile. On the basis of the theory of galactic rotation, and from optical data like those discussed in Chapters 4 and 5, we may derive a model for the distribution of mass and velocities in our Milky Way system; Table 4 and Fig. 56 are based on models of this sort. Such a model may be obtained from known data of stellar distribution and from observed motions parallel and at right angles to the galactic plane. Special groups of stars, like cluster-type variables, for example, which are observed at large distances from the galactic plane, enable us to make a fair estimate about the distribution of mass and velocity in our Milky Way system. We thus obtain the necessary data for a table that gives the variation with distance from the galactic center of the circular velocity of rotation in our galaxy. With such a table, we may now proceed, for any direction in the plane of the Milky Way as observed from the earth and sun, to plot the radial velocity of approach or recession that may be expected for a hydrogen cloud at a particular distance from the sun. In turn, we may estimate on the basis of the observed radial velocity of any particular cloud what is the most likely value for the distance from that cloud to the sun. In this fashion, Oort, van de Hulst, and Muller were able to assign to each intensity peak in the 21-centimeter profiles, observed separately for a given galactic longitude in the galactic plane, distances corresponding to the observed radial velocities of the maxima of intensity. We shall see in the next chapter that the analysis of the curves in Fig. 107 has resulted in a remarkable extension of our knowledge regarding the spiral structure of our Milky Way system.

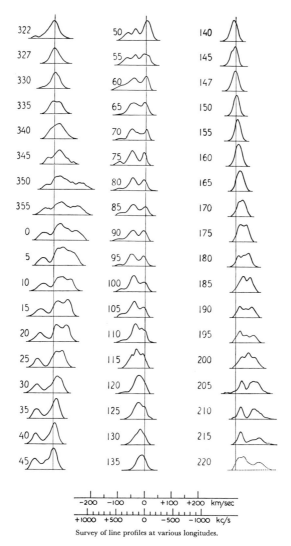

Survey of line profiles at various longitudes.

Fig. 107.   21-cm profiles, obtained by van de Hulst, Muller, and Oort, for the entire range of galactic longitude $l = 322°$ to $l = 220°$ for points 5° apart along the galactic circle. The effect of certain spiral features can be readily traced by comparing a given profile with that which precedes or follows it. The scale of radial velocities is printed at the bottom of the diagram. (From the *Bulletin of the Astronomical Institutes of the Netherlands.*)

We found earlier that for the direction of the galactic center and the anticenter one might not be able to penetrate to very great distances from our sun. The 21-centimeter fog might simply be too thick. This limitation, however, does not hold for directions in which radial velocity shifts are observed. To show why this is so, let us look for a moment at a model of two hydrogen clouds, one with zero radial velocity relative to the sun, the other with appreciable velocity of approach. If the first cloud were optically thick and if the second cloud had also no appreciable radial velocity relative to the earth and sun, then the radiation from the second cloud would never be able to reach us. But if it happens that our second cloud has a considerable velocity of approach, then the radio quanta emitted by it will all have wavelengths considerably shorter than the normal unshifted wavelength of the 21-centimeter line. The quanta from the second can therefore not be absorbed by the neutral hydrogen atoms in the first cloud and they will simply pass through it unhindered on their way to our sun.

The first studies by Oort, van de Hulst, and Muller have already revealed much about the structure of our system that was hitherto unknown, but some difficult problems of interpretation still lie ahead. It can readily be seen that for the outer parts of our galaxy a given velocity of approach or recession will correspond only to a cloud at one given distance, but the same is not true for the inner parts of our galaxy. Observations at galactic longitudes differing by more than 90° from the longitude to the galactic center will give unambiguous information regarding the spiral structure in these directions for distances from the galactic center equal to or greater than that of our sun. But the analysis is not so straightforward for the half of the Milky Way within 90° of the galactic center. The interpretation of the intensity distribution for velocities corresponding to smaller distances than that of the sun from the center will generally not give a clear-cut picture. Here we find that two different distances may be assigned to one single observed radial velocity. The origin of the mixed radiation can be disentangled with the aid of observations at different galactic latitudes for each galactic longitude: the radiations originating at great distances are much more closely concentrated to the plane of the Milky Way than those from relatively nearby clouds.

Studies of the 21-centimeter radiation are giving information on many subjects not directly related to spiral structure. We have al-

Fig. 108.   The 80-foot radio telescope at Dwingelo in Holland, with altazimuth mounting.

ready referred in Chapter 7 to the important problems relating to the constancy of the ratio between the densities of gas and dust. Here the techniques of optical and radio astronomy are being used side by side in the study of a physical problem in our Milky Way system.

There are many astrophysical problems awaiting attack by a skillful blending of the techniques of optical and radio astronomy. We mention two of them.

The first is the problem of the relative distribution of hydrogen, neutral and ionized, and cosmic dust in the section of Orion. At a distance of about 1500 light-years from the sun we find the diffuse Great Nebula in Orion, the Horsehead Nebula with its associated dust, the giant faint emission ring discovered by Barnard, and many related features. From Adams's studies of multiple interstellar absorption lines much has been learned about the fine structure of the gas clouds and the distribution of their radial velocities. What does the study of the 21-centimeter profiles for this section tell us about the presence and the velocities of the neutral hydrogen? A study by Menon at the Agassiz Station shows that there is an abundance of neutral hydrogen associated with the ionized hydrogen. According to Menon's estimates, the total mass of neutral hydrogen is equiv-

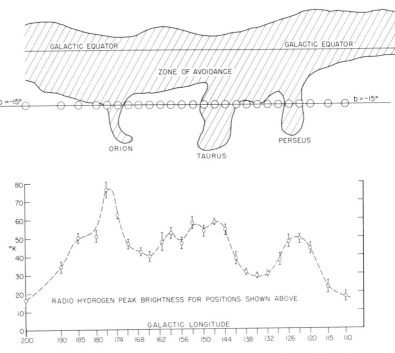

Fig. 109. Neutral hydrogen associated with dark nebulosity. The diagram by Lilley shows in the top half the outline of Hubble's Zone of Avoidance of galactic obscuration. Note the extensions south of the Milky Way in Orion, Taurus, and Perseus. For the positions marked by the open circles at galactic latitude $b = -15°$, Lilley has measured with the aid of the 24-foot radio telescope at Agassiz Station the intensity of the 21-cm signals, with the results shown in the lower half of the figure. Obviously the strongest signals come from the direction of greatest obscuration.

alent to between 60,000 and 100,000 solar masses, which may be contrasted with the total mass of the Orion emission nebula, generally estimated to be of the order of only 1000 solar masses! Moreover, Menon's studies suggest that the whole Orion gas complex is expanding at a rate of about 10 kilometers per second and that it is probably in rotation.

A second variety of astrophysical problem that requires study by optical and radio techniques is the cloud structure of the interstellar gaseous medium. The multiple interstellar absorption lines, discovered by Adams and studied recently by Münch, have shown that much of the interstellar absorption takes place in fairly dense gas clouds of relatively small size. But the spectroscopic data give little indication as to probable sizes. By the 21-centimeter technique, we may search for possible radiation from the neutral hydro-

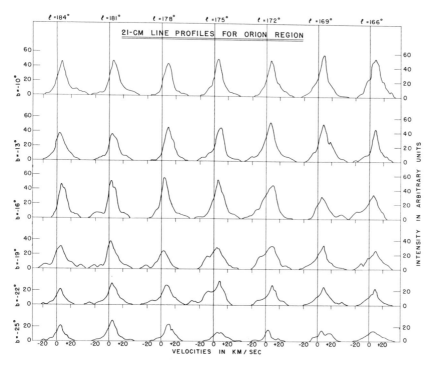

Fig. 110.   21-cm profiles for the Orion region. Menon has used the 24-foot radio telescope at Agassiz Station to obtain profiles for the huge Orion complex of neutral atomic hydrogen. His analysis indicates that we have here a mass of interstellar hydrogen of the order of 60,000 to 100,000 solar masses in slow rotation and expanding at a rate of about 8 km/sec. The positions are indicated by their galactic longitudes (l) and latitudes (b).

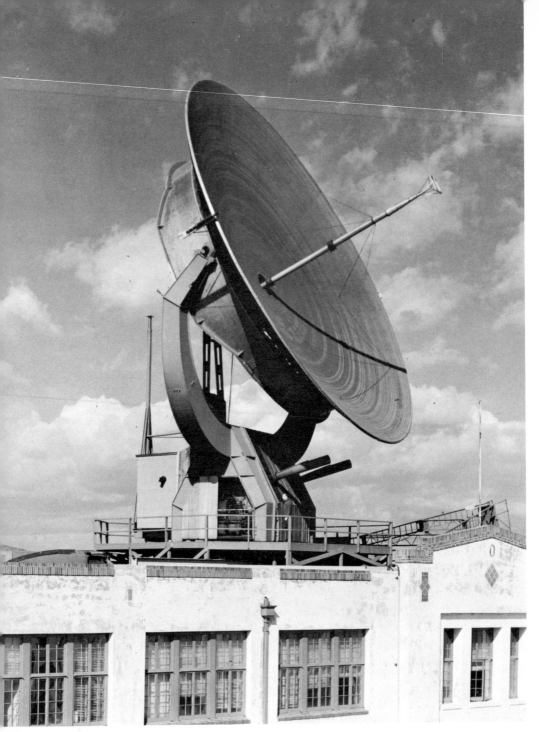

Fig. 111.   The 50-foot steerable antenna of the U. S. Naval Research Laboratory. This antenna on top of the NRL Building at Washington, D. C. has a solid surface and is mounted in altazimuth fashion. (U. S. Navy photograph.)

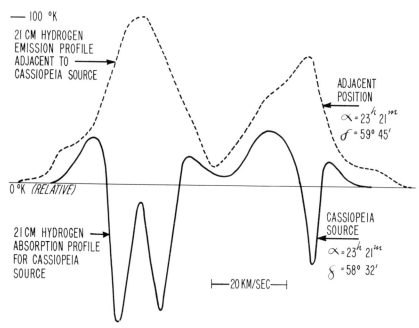

Fig. 112.   21-cm profiles for discrete radio sources. Lilley and McClain at the Naval Research Laboratory have determined profiles for a number of discrete radio sources, notably for the Cassiopeia source (upper) and the direction of the galactic center (lower).

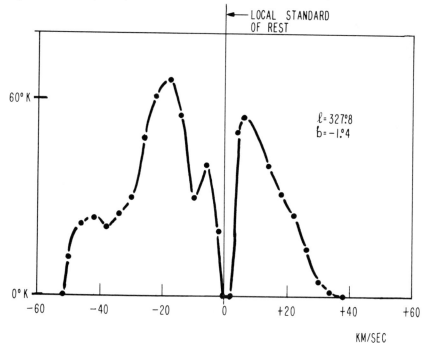

Fig. 113.   The 60-foot George R. Agassiz radio telescope. In (a) are shown the expanded aluminum-mesh surface of the 60-foot paraboloid reflector and the horn feed, supported at the focus by three fiberglass struts, which receives the galactic or extragalactic radio radiation;

(*b*) shows the equatorial mounting of the telescope. This latest addition to the Harvard equipment for research in radio astronomy was dedicated on April 28, 1956. (*Sky and Telescope* photograph by Robert E. Cox.)

gen in these same clouds and attempt to find an upper limit to their dimensions. Lawrence has found evidence that in at least two cases an optical cloud discovered by Münch can be traced in the 21-centimeter radiation.

The present limiting factor in the radio work is the aperture of the antenna. A little wisp of a hydrogen cloud placed in the line of sight between the star and the sun and earth will produce one of Münch's absorption lines, but, to be detectable with a 24-foot radio reflector, the same cloud must cover at least an area of 1° diameter in the sky. Once the 60-foot, 80-foot, 140-foot, 250-foot, . . . , 600-foot antennas go into operation, we shall really be able to tackle this problem and understand the cloud structure of the interstellar gas.

The fine structure of the spiral arms of our galaxy needs much study in the future. The Leiden results, supplemented by those obtained for the southern Milky Way by Kerr and associates at Sydney, have given us the broad features of the spiral pattern for our Milky Way system. We now ask what are the widths of the arms; is there evidence for branching; what are the spreads in the velocities inside an arm? To answer these questions requires radio equipment with high resolution in frequency attached to large paraboloid antennas. And to do the job well, as has been shown through the researches of Matthews, Westerhout, and Helfer and Tatel, one requires, along with the radio data, more and more precise optical information about the distances to O–B aggregates and associated gaseous nebulosities. Again, optical and radio research must go hand in hand.

We touch finally, but very briefly, upon absorption features in the 21-centimeter profiles. These were first recorded definitely by Hagen, Lilley, and McClain at the Naval Research Laboratory in Washington, who observed unexpectedly sharp absorption features for the direction of some of the strong known continuous sources, Cassiopeia, Taurus, and the direction of the galactic center. Apparently these absorption lines are formed very much in the manner of the absorption lines in a star's spectrum, or of the pair of sodium absorption lines shown in the traditional elementary physics experiment. Since the discrete radio sources subtend only small angles in the sky, the absorption techniques permit, with the aid of 21-centimeter equipment, the search for much smaller neutral hydrogen clouds than are now detectable in emission.

The search for other lines should be pressed because from them we may be able to derive important information regarding the abundance and evolution of the species of atoms that inhabit interstellar space. We have already noted the Soviet discovery of the line from the deuterium (heavy hydrogen) atom with a wavelength of 92 centimeters, which still requires confirmation. Among other possibilities are those first mentioned by Shklovsky, who suggested that it might be profitable to look for lines of molecular hydrides such as OH, NH, CH, and CH^+. Townes has especially urged the search for radiation from the OH molecule, which may be detectable— though very faint—near a wavelength of 18 centimeters; a recent very careful attempt at the discovery of the OH radiation by Lilley and Barrett at the Naval Research Laboratory failed to show anything positive.

9

The Spiral Structure
of the Galaxy

Outline of Our Galaxy

During the past decade research on the structure of the Milky Way system has progressed rapidly. The authors could hardly have guessed in 1945, upon the completion of the second edition of the present book, that in the third edition they would have to find room for chapters on radio astronomy and on the spiral structure of the galaxy. We have seen in the preceding chapter how in a relatively short time radio astronomy has made for itself a permanent niche in Milky Way research. We shall show in the present chapter that we may now speak with some confidence of the spiral structure of our own galaxy.

In Chapters 4 and 5, we dealt with problems relating to the general outline of the structure of our galaxy. The picture that emerges is one in which our sun is located at a distance of approximately 27,000 light-years from the center. The galactic center lies somewhere between galactic longitude 325° and 330°, 1° or 2° south of

229

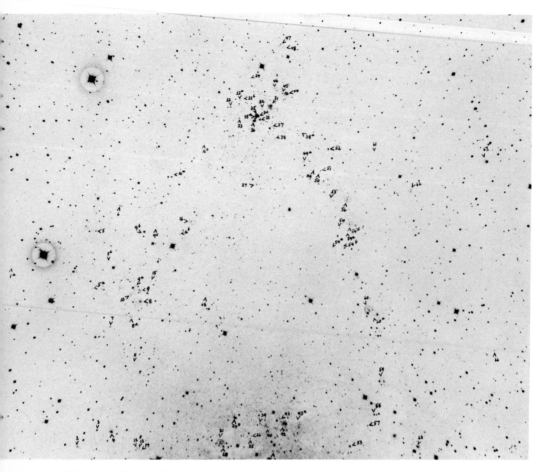

Fig. 114. Outer spiral structure of the Andromeda Nebula. The negative of a Mount Wilson photograph shows a section near the upper left-hand corner of Fig. 12. Dr. Walter Baade has given the following information about this photograph: Emission nebulae along one of the outer spiral arms of Messier 31, photographed in Hα light. At the bottom (center) emission nebulosities belonging to the next inner arm are seen, whereas Nos. 66, 67, and 1a are scattered members of one of the outermost arms of Messier 31. (4-hour exposure at 100-inch telescope by Baade.)

the galactic circle, in the constellation Sagittarius; the most recent determination of the radio center by Kraus places it at $l = 327°8$, $b = -1°4$. Our sun is a fairly average, faint, and inconspicuous star located in the outer fringe of the galaxy. The sun moves in a nearly circular orbit with a speed of the order of 140 miles per second and takes about 200,000,000 years to complete one circuit around the center of the galaxy.

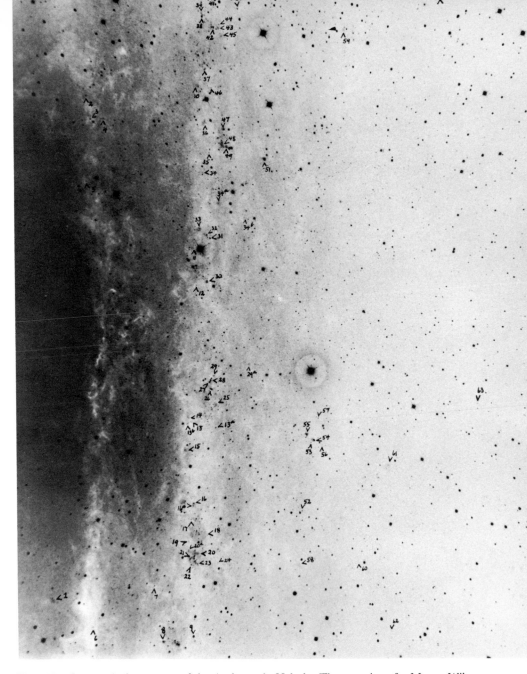

Fig. 115. Inner spiral structure of the Andromeda Nebula. The negative of a Mount Wilson photograph shows a section to the right of the center of the Andromeda nebula as shown in Fig. 12. Dr. Walter Baade has given the following information about this photograph: Spiral arms of Messier 31, silhouetted against the bright nuclear region. Note that the emission nebulosities of the innermost spiral arm (Nos. 2, 3, 4, 5, and 6) lie in a dark lane; similarly, the emission nebulosities of the next spiral arm. This shows convincingly that the spiral arms are made up of large dust clouds which become conspicuous in this position because they cut off the light of the underlying Population II. (4-hour exposure at 100-inch telescope by Baade.)

The available evidence from galactic rotation and from the distributions and motions of special classes of stars, like the cluster-type variables, which travel to great distances from the galactic plane, shows that our galaxy has in all probability an extended nucleus. We may think of the inner portions of the galaxy as composed of a lens-shaped central body of approximately constant density, which rotates at an nearly uniform angular rate and whose outer edge is not more than 6000 or 7000 light-years from the sun. According to this picture the nucleus would have the shape of a flattened spheroid with a semimajor axis of about 20,000 light-years and a semiminor axis of 6000 to 7000 light-years; Oort and his associates have estimated the average density in the nuclear region to be about twice that for the vicinity of the sun. There may well be a central core of high density inside the large nuclear spheroid and the total mass of this core may be as high as one-tenth of that of the whole galaxy.

We are still somewhat in the dark concerning the detailed structure of the galactic nucleus and its population since it is unfortunately rather effectively hidden from our view by nearby dense overlying obscuring clouds. The appearance of the Milky Way in Sagittarius would certainly be very different if it were not for these dark nebulae. Only the infrared and radio wavelengths penetrate the cosmic haze and indicate to us that the visually most brilliant section of the entire Milky Way, that of the Large Star Cloud of Sagittarius, marks only one edge of the very extended nuclear region.

Our galaxy is probably a spiral of intermediate type, not unlike the giant spiral in Andromeda. We possess a well-developed nucleus, but we are by no means all nucleus and no arms! Our sun is located in the region of spiral structure of our galaxy. We are surrounded in most directions in the galactic plane by luminous O and B stars, extended emission nebulae, and plentiful cosmic dust, all of them commonly associated either with galaxies showing spiral structure or with young irregular galaxies such as the Large Magellanic Cloud. It seems settled beyond reasonable doubt that we are not a part of an irregular galaxy. For the past 20 years few astronomers have doubted that our galaxy possesses spiral structure, but it is only quite recently that the actual tracing of the spiral arms of our galaxy has begun.

Our sun's position in the midst of the spiral structure and very close to the central plane of our galaxy provides the principal stum-

Fig. 116. The spiral in Triangulum. The photograph with the 200-inch Hale reflector shows the central section of the spiral galaxy.

bling block to a precise tracing of the spiral structure of our galaxy. The task would be simpler if we could only remove ourselves to a point 25,000 or 50,000 light-years above or below the central plane of the galaxy, for then we should presumably see the entire spiral pattern spread openly before our eyes. But for better or for worse we are in the midst of the spiral show and our task of tracing the spiral arms is made even more difficult by the presence of dark nebulosity distributed irregularly throughout the galactic plane. About 10 years ago Baade pointed out that our situation seemed hopeless unless we were to preface the study of the spiral structure in our own galaxy with careful studies of the properties of spiral arms in other galaxies, noting especially what types of objects are commonly associated with spiral structure in them. This was eminently sound advice and we shall preface the present report of the current status of research on the spiral structure of our own galaxy with a brief description of what is known concerning the spiral structure in nearby galaxies, notably in the Andromeda spiral.

*   *

*

Properties of
Spiral Galaxies   In 1951 Baade and Mayall summarized the information obtained for the great spiral in Andromeda, Messier 31, from photographs made with the 100-inch Hooker and 200-inch Hale reflectors. The results of their studies were published before the revision of the distance scale for galaxies had been announced, but it is not a difficult matter to correct some of their statements for the effects of revisions of distance and we have done so. For the Andromeda spiral, the arms stand out clearly on normal blue-sensitive plates. They are much less pronounced on photographs made with yellow-sensitive emulsions or emulsions sensitive primarily to the infrared, but they are again neatly marked on red-sensitive plates with filters selected to permit passage of the light from the Hα hydrogen line. A closer inspection of the Mount Wilson and Palomar photographs shows that the spiral arms can be traced most effectively by means of single blue supergiants of types O and B, by clusters and associations of O and B stars, by patches of hydrogen Hα emission, and by absorbing and reddening cosmic dust. Galactic Cepheids of fairly long periods are also found associated with spiral structure. Four spiral arms can be traced on the north side of the nucleus and five

Fig. 117.   The spiral in Pisces. One of the best examples of a well-developed spiral galaxy.
(200-inch Hale reflector, Palomar.)

Fig. 118.   An edge-on spiral galaxy in Coma Berenices. (From a photograph made with the 200-inch Hale Palomar reflector.)

on the south side, and two can be followed to well inside the central body of Messier 31. Isolated patches of blue-white stars may be traced to beyond 150 minutes of arc from the center, that is, to distances of the order of 70,000 light-years from the center of this galaxy (the recent estimates place the Andromeda spiral at a distance close to 1,600,000 light-years from our sun). The cosmic dust appears to be largely localized in the spiral arms, but to be most dense at the inner arcs of these arms. Very close to the edge of the nuclear region, the spiral arms may be traced most effectively through absorption features, which persist even where the presence of gaseous emission is no longer evident. Baade has found that the

Fig. 119.   A grand view of the Southern Milky Way from the Southern Cross to
Altair, photographed by Code and Houck with the Greenstein-Henyey wide-angle
camera set up at the Boyden Station: (a) in blue light, (b) in infrared light. The
infrared photograph shows especially well how the absorption associated with the
northern and southern Rifts in the Milky Way produces the appearance of an
equatorial band of obscuration like that shown in the edge-on galaxy of Fig. 118.
In (a) the Southern Cross and the Coalsack are shown near the right-hand edge
of the photograph. Then follow the two bright stars Alpha and Beta Cantauri.
The Sagittarius Cloud and the dark nebulae of Ophiuchus and Scorpius are
directly above the center of the photograph (the three black streaks are produced
by metal fin supports in the camera). To the left and above the center is the
Scutum Cloud; Altair is the bright star fairly close to the left-hand edge of the
photograph. (Courtesy of the Washburn Observatory of the University of
Wisconsin.)

association between dust and O and B stars is an intricate one; together they generally mark the beginning of a spiral arm fairly close to the nucleus.

One should be careful not to oversimplify or overstylize the properties of spiral arms in galaxies outside our own. In Messier 31 one finds that the spiral arms are generally quite narrow. The width of a typical section of a spiral arm is generally of the order of 2500 light-years and the distance between the arms is of the order of 10,000 to 12,000 light-years. Frequently, however, one finds short branches protruding from the main spiral arm, and in some spirals these branches may be strong and persist over fairly long distances. To appreciate fully the problem that faces the investigator of the spiral structure in our own system, the reader will do well to inspect with care all of the photographs in the present volume and to imagine for himself what difficulties he would encounter if he were placed at various locations in or between the spiral arms in spiral galaxies other than our own. It will soon become evident that the situation may be quite complex.

It is clear from the above description that O and B stars, singly or in clusters and associations, Hα emission nebulae, and clouds of cosmic dust are "spiral tracers" of first importance. We should add to this list the so called W stars, stars that are of high temperature with extended atmospheres showing emission lines. The status of the long-period Cepheids is not quite so clear. While these do favor the spiral arms, they occur as well in between the arms and they seem to be considerably more bunched than the other spiral features. We are at present similarly in doubt about the precise status of the galactic clusters not primarily composed of O and B stars. Most clusters of A stars, as well as the A giants themselves, are too faint for effective study in galaxies outside our own, and their relation to the spiral structure remains for the present uncertain. Whereas the normal red giants appear to be generally associated with Population II, and are therefore characteristic of the nucleus and of the regions between the spiral arms, there is a possibility that the brightest red supergiants may follow the spiral structure. The status of these second-class spiral tracers will probably have to be settled from studies inside our own galaxy, at least for stars with absolute magnitudes $M = -1$ and fainter. For the initial tracing of the spiral arms of our own galaxy, we should therefore depend for the time being on the first-class spiral tracers.

*   *

*

The first insight into the spiral structure of our galaxy came from an investigation by Morgan of the Yerkes Observatory. In a paper presented at the Christmas meetings (December 1951) of the American Astronomical Society, Morgan spoke of the results obtained from a collaborative effort involving several observatories; Morgan, Nassau, and their associates at the Warner and Swasey Observatory in Cleveland had made an extensive search for O and B stars along the northern Milky Way. Spectral types and luminosity classes for most of the newly discovered stars had been determined by Morgan at the Yerkes Observatory; Whitford and Code of the Washburn Observatory of the University of Wisconsin had photoelectrically determined colors for these same stars. Finally, Morgan, Sharpless, and Osterbrock had photographed the Milky Way within reach from the Yerkes Observatory with the aid of the fast Greenstein-Henyey camera and had succeeded (see Chapter 7) in locating the most marked regions of hydrogen Hα emission. Sections of two spiral arms were clearly indicated and there was a suggestion of a third arm as well.

Spiral Structure of Our Galaxy: Optical Evidence

Morgan's first arm, which he called the *Orion Arm*, is observed between galactic longitudes 40° and 180° to 190°, that is, all the way from Cygnus through Cepheus and Cassiopeia's chair past Perseus and Orion to Monoceros. Morgan suggests that the Great Rift of the Milky Way marks actually a part of the inner dark lane of this spiral arm. Our sun is placed close to the inner edge of this arm. Morgan traced this arm over a distance close to 12,000 light-years and found it to be about 1200 light-years wide. He estimates that our sun is not quite at the inner edge but rather 100 to 200 light-years inside the Orion arm.

Morgan's second spiral arm is about 7000 light-years from the sun and it can be traced between galactic longitudes 70° and 140°. The width and length of the observed section of this second arm appears to be not unlike that of the first one, but the density of concentrations of emission nebulosity is less for the second arm than for the first; the reverse seems to be true for neutral atomic hydrogen which the 21-centimeter measures show to be very abundant in the second arm. It appears to be the outermost arm that may be readily traced by optical means. Since the double cluster in Perseus is the most conspicuous feature in the second arm, Morgan gave it the name *Perseus Arm*.

Morgan and his associates also suggested in 1951 the presence of a third arm closer to the galactic center than our sun. This inner arm, known as the *Sagittarius Arm*, could not be charted very well by northern observers, but the task has been completed from observatories in the Southern Hemisphere. Bok, Bester, and Wade found from the southern Hα survey (see Chapter 7) at the Boyden Station that hydrogen emission patches are strong and abundant for the section between galactic longitudes 300° and 345°, in the constellations Norma, Scorpius, and Sagittarius. This is a very complex section of the Milky Way. The band of highest star concentration—which includes the Great Star Cloud of Sagittarius—lies here several degrees (up to 4° in a few places) to the south of the geometric galactic equator, which is defined as the great circle on the celestial sphere that passes most nearly through the points of highest star concentration averaged for the whole sky. The emission patches, however, do not occur in the regions richest in stars, but fall almost exactly along the geometric galactic equator. In several places they are seen either through nearby obscuring dust clouds or projected against more distant dust clouds.

Emission features are very weak or absent between galactic longitude 265° and 300°, from the Southern Cross to Norma, and here we have almost certainly a gap in the southern spiral structure. Very strong features are again observed between 250° and 265°, in the Carina section of the Milky Way, which all along has been the primary candidate for a spiral knot in our galaxy. O and B stars, W stars, and emission nebulae are present in the Carina section in an abundance that is nowhere nearly equaled in other sections of the Milky Way, north or south. At galactic longitude 250°, in Vela, a sharp break in the spiral structure is observed. A very interesting situation is found in the section between 180° and 240°, that is, from Monoceros through Canis Major and Puppis to Vela. Between 180° and 200°, reaching southward just about as far as Sirius, we find a clear extension of Morgan's Orion Arm. Very little hydrogen emission nebulosity is observed between galactic longitudes 200° and 220°, but a strong nebulous region is found again in galactic longitudes 220° and 240°, near the borderline between Puppis and Vela. Here Gum at the Commonwealth Observatory of Australia has discovered an extended region of diffuse nebulosity, the existence of which has been fully confirmed by Bok, Bester, and Wade. There are at least five recognized centers of emission nebulosity in this section, some of them relatively near the sun, and

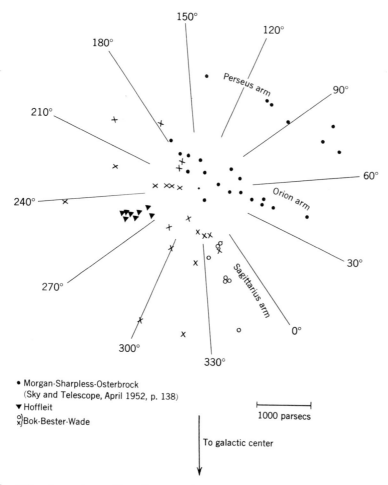

Fig. 120.   An early working diagram of spiral structure. The sun is at the center of the diagram and the lines radiating from it indicate galactic longitudes in the galactic plane, separated by 30°. The circles centered upon the sun have radii of 1000, 2000, and 3000 parsecs (1000 parsecs = 3258 light-years); the galactic center would be at 27,000 light-years from the sun, hence on the eighth circle outward. The dots mark the positions of the emission nebulae studied by Morgan, Sharpless, and Osterbrock (Christmas 1951) and these showed clearly for the first time sections of the Orion and Perseus arms. The presence of an inner arm, the Sagittarius arm, was suggested by the northern observers and this was confirmed by Hoffleit (triangles) and by Bok, Bester, and Wade (crosses and open circles) from observations made at the Boyden Station.

these may probably constitute a short spike protruding from the primary Orion Arm discovered by Morgan. Figure 120 summarizes the situation with regard to spiral structure as derived from studies of O and B stars and associated hydrogen nebulosity. The available evidence seems to point strongly to the presence of three observable sections of spiral arms within 10,000 light-years of our sun. The length of each observed section is also roughly 10,000 light-years. While the research to date covers a considerable portion of the Milky Way system, we should remember that the distance from the sun to the galactic center is 27,000 light-years and that by far the greater portion of the Milky Way remains as yet unexplored. While we may expect in the future more detailed and more precise information, derived from photographic and spectrographic observations, regarding the spiral structure in the vicinity of the sun, it does not seem likely that we shall be able to observe O and B stars and associated nebulosity to distances very much greater than 15,000 light-years toward the galactic center. We must therefore turn to other means if we wish to obtain information regarding spiral structure at greater distances, and the techniques of radio astronomy must obviously come to our rescue.

Spiral Structure
of Our Galaxy:
21-Centimeter
Evidence

*   *

*

In Chapter 8 we have already described in detail how, from observations of the line profiles of the 21-centimeter line of neutral hydrogen, one may by radio methods obtain information regarding the distribution of neutral hydrogen in our Milky Way system. The basic observational material for each direction in the Milky Way consists of a line profile, which gives the distribution of intensity of the radio radiation from neutral hydrogen as a function of the frequency or wavelength. Since all hydrogen atoms emit radiation of exactly identical wavelength, a difference between the observed wavelength and the normal wavelength for an atom at rest will be a measure of the velocity of approach or recession of the emitting hydrogen. We may thus translate the horizontal wavelength scale of these line profiles into a scale of velocities of approach or recession. If we assume a model for the velocity distribution in our rotating galaxy, then any given radial velocity of approach or recession for a particular direction will indicate a position for the

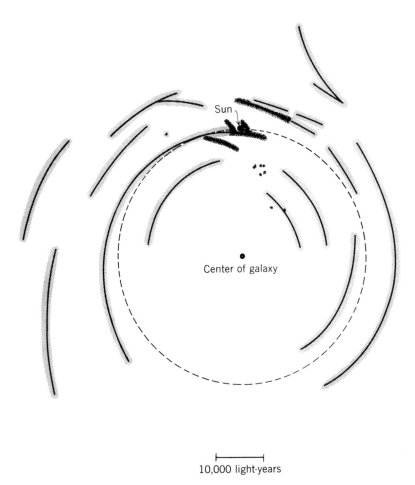

Sun

Center of galaxy

10,000 light-years

Fig. 121.   The diagram, prepared by F. J. Kerr of the Radiophysics Laboratory in Sydney, shows in schematic form the available evidence regarding the spiral features of our galaxy by combining the data from the Northern and Southern Hemispheres. The radio data (shaded lines) for the Northern Hemisphere are from the material gathered by the Leiden observers; those for the Southern Hemisphere are provisional data from the Sydney survey. The optical data (black lines and dots) were assembled by C. S. Gum from his own and Morgan's observations.

emitting atom at a certain definite distance from the sun. Since neutral hydrogen is apparently associated with the spiral arms, the presence of two or more maxima in a given radio line profile may be taken to indicate concentration of hydrogen at two (or sometimes more) specific points in our Milky Way for a given line of sight. We may plot the derived distances to the neutral hydrogen concentration for all observed directions in the Milky Way and we can then see whether or not these plotted points form a spiral pattern. It is in this fashion that Oort, van de Hulst, and Muller have analyzed the curves reproduced in Fig. 107, with the results shown in Fig. 121.

The Oort, van de Hulst, and Muller diagram of spiral structure, as derived from 21-centimeter line studies and as shown in Fig. 121 is one of the truly historic diagrams of Milky Way research. The reader will remember that earlier in this chapter we mentioned that it seemed almost hopeless to extend our knowledge of spiral structure for our Milky Way system by optical methods to distances beyond 15,000 light-years from our sun. But the radio methods are not nearly so limited in distance, and it will be noted that the Leiden group has already succeeded in locating a section of a spiral arm that stretches halfway around our galaxy to distances of the order of 50,000 light-years from our sun. This is as far away from the center of the galaxy as our sun is but on the opposite side.

Radio astronomy is so young a science that we are only beginning to realize its full potentialities. At the moment the analysis of the profiles for the inner regions of our galaxy seems to be beset with difficulties, largely because a wavelength indicating a particular velocity of approach or recession may come from clouds at two different distances from the sun. With time and patience, and especially with improved techniques of observation, these problems should be solved and here the very large parabolic radio antennas with their greater resolving power will undoubtedly play an important role. The important thing now to stress is that through the separate researches of Baade, Morgan, and Oort the whole field of research of the spiral structure of our Milky Way has burst wide open. Where a few years ago we seemed to be up against a blank wall of discouragement, we are now in an era of rapidly developing research.

*   *
*

Further
Evidence   Confirmation of Morgan's suggestion regarding the presence of two observable sections of spiral arms in the northern Milky Way has been obtained by Guido Münch, at the California Institute of Technology, who has investigated the problems connected with multi-

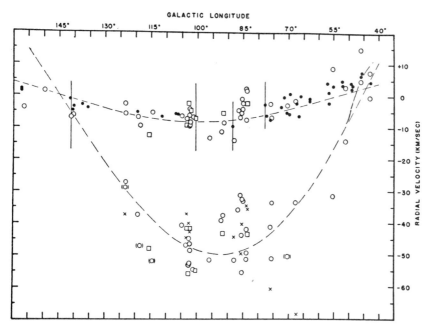

Fig. 122.   Interstellar absorption lines and spiral structure. The diagram represents the results of Münch of radial-velocity observations for interstellar lines. The
stars are all close to the galactic circle and their galactic longitudes are shown
horizontally. Vertically we find the derived radial velocities of the measured components. The open circles are for the strong component of the interstellar K line,
the open squares for the interstellar sodium D lines. The widths of a few lines are
indicated by the thin vertical lines. The open circles and squares refer to interstellar lines observed in the spectra of stars at least 3500 light-years from the sun,
whereas the solid dots are for interstellar lines observed for stars that are nearer to
the sun. The crosses refer to a few isolated observations of stellar radial velocities.
The two curved arcs (dashed) have been drawn in by Münch to show what
galactic rotation shifts in radial velocity might be expected at distances of the
order of 1300 and 10,000 light-years from the sun; the manner in which these
curves represent the observed radial velocities suggests that the interstellar clouds
are either in the Orion arm (1300-light-year curve) or in the Perseus arm
(10,000-light-year curve), but not in between.

ple interstellar lines. With the aid of the new coudé spectrograph
of the 200-inch Hale telescope, Münch has surveyed a large section
of the northern Milky Way and has been able to show that the
majority of the observed distant stars have multiple interstellar
lines (Fig. 122). On the basis of the theory of galactic rotation, the
observed radial velocity of approach or recession of a given line
component places the corresponding interstellar hydrogen cloud at
a given distance from the sun. When Münch plots the array of

distances for the observed clouds these are found to follow closely two sections of the spiral arms discovered by Morgan.

There is considerable evidence to suggest that local structure plays a role in addition to the general spiral features for the vicinity of the sun. For example, according to the simplified spiral picture, there should be a region of low density between our sun and the Carina concentration of O and B stars. Almost exactly the opposite is true, for studies at Harvard have shown that the region of greatest concentration of the B8–A0 stars occurs at distances of the order of 1000 to 3000 light-years from the sun in Carina, whereas the spiral structure is most likely located at a distance of at least 5000 light-years from the sun for this particular direction. Because of the present uncertainty of the precise status of the A stars as spiral tracers, it seems rather pointless to philosophize now on the significance of the high density of the B8–A0 stars for this direction, but the observations are certainly indicative of structure not consistent with the simple spiral picture. Several instances of marked deviation from the basic spiral pattern have been noted by Weaver.

In 1937 and 1938, Vashakidze and Oort drew attention to the possibility of obtaining evidence for spiral structure from stellar distribution in high and intermediate latitudes, where interstellar absorption and irregularities in stellar distribution presumably would play a smaller role than at low galactic latitudes. Oort at that time drew a diagram that indicated the presence of two spiral arms and according to which our sun would be located between these two arms. Oort's hypothesis was examined in considerable detail by Kukarkin and Parenago of the Soviet Union and while they agree in general terms with the spiral picture as proposed by Oort, they suggest that our sun may be located in a separate small local condensation, slightly elongated in the direction from Carina to Cygnus. It is as yet by no means clear how these local structures will fit into the general picture of the spiral structure of our galaxy.

To conclude this chapter, we should stress once again that it is wrong in principle to expect the spiral structure to conform to a simple unified pattern. Complex patterns of structure, with all sorts of spikes protruding from the principal arms, are observed in spiral galaxies like Messier 31, 51, and 83. We shall see in the concluding chapter that the O and B stars, which, along with the interstellar gas and dust, are the primary tracers of spiral structure for our part of the galaxy, are of recent origin, probably formed less than

Fig. 123.   The spiral Messier 81. This photograph, made with the 200-inch Hale Palomar reflector, shows one of the finest bright spiral galaxies.

a quarter or so of a galactic revolution ago. If this is the case, then there may have existed earlier patterns of spiral structure—now devoid of the very luminous O and B stars—which through the shearing forces of galactic rotation should have already partly dissolved themselves into the general galactic substratum, but which may possibly still be traced through the distribution of A stars and stars of later types. The concentrations of A stars that are observed without attending associations of O and B stars (in Carina, for instance) may be remnants of earlier spiral structure, of *fossil spiral arms,* so to speak.

Our primary task for the next few years is to build equipment—especially radio equipment—capable of tracing with precision the spiral structure of our galaxy. While there is always room for theorizing, the emphasis must first of all be on careful observation and unbiased analysis of the observations.

10

Our Changing Galaxy

Our Milky Way is changing constantly. The changes are slow and gradual and not easy to detect, for on the cosmic scale our span of life represents but a fleeting moment. Whereas the regular year serves as a convenient unit for time measurement on the earth and for the recording of the changes in the positions of the planets, we shall have to turn to a larger unit in considering cosmic evolution. For this purpose we choose the *cosmic year,* which is the time of one revolution of our sun around the center of our galaxy. One cosmic year measures very nearly 200,000,000 of our familiar solar years.

What changes take place if we think in terms of cosmic years? The stars of our galaxy are continually being reshuffled, for as small a difference in velocity as 1 mile per second will, in the course of 1,000,000 years, or 1/200 cosmic year, serve to separate two stars by 5 light-years. In the course of 1 cosmic year groups of stars may be dissipated, other groups may be born anew and the spiral appearance of our galaxy may undergo profound changes.

In addition to these purely mechanical changes, the physical make-up of our Milky Way system may not remain the same over intervals of the order of 1 cosmic year. In the deep interiors of the sun and stars the nuclear energy sources are constantly at work, but they are not inexhaustible and the rates at which they produce radiant energy may in the long run vary considerably. The O and B stars use up their large yet limited supplies of nuclear energy at such prodigious rates that their present lavish displays cannot have persisted for more than a fraction of a cosmic year. It seems almost certain that they were formed rather recently on the cosmic scale, that is, much less than 1 cosmic year ago. We are thus led to consider not only problems of the evolution of stars as stars, but also possible processes of star birth. What role does the interstellar gas and dust play in the formation of new stars and to what extent do the stars replenish their not inexhaustible supplies of interstellar matter? These are some of the questions that will concern us in the present concluding chapter. But first, we shall inquire into problems related to the appropriate time scale for cosmic evolution.

*   *

*

Large-Scale
Changes

The fact that the individual stars are in rapid motion does not by itself imply that the system as a whole is changing appreciably. The red and white blood corpuscles are always racing through our veins and arteries, but the amount of blood in any particular vein does not as a whole vary greatly in the course of days or months. In the same fashion, the configuration of a knot in a spiral arm might remain the same over long intervals of time; while some stars move out of a particular grouping, other stars may replace them.

If the distribution of positions and motions in a galaxy suffers no large-scale changes, we say that the stellar system is in *dynamical equilibrium*. Even if we should disregard real evolutionary changes—which we can certainly not do when we are dealing with the O and B stars—the state of dynamical equilibrium will not be a permanent one. For a particular group of stars, the state of dynamical equilibrium would probably survive for as long as 100 cosmic years, but not for 1000 or 10,000 cosmic years. Chance encounters with passing stars will begin to have their effects over such long intervals of time and the state of dynamical equilibrium will be upset, to be replaced by the more thoroughly mixed state of *statistical equilibrium,* which is more permanent. Detailed predictions for the future are not possible, but certain trends may be predicted and from them we may gain an insight into the time scale of dynamical evolution. We may, with considerable hesitation, attempt even to probe back into the dim past of the origin of our galaxy.

*   *

*

When Stars Meet

How often, on the average, does a star come sufficiently close to our sun to change the sun's course appreciably? We know fairly well the separations and velocities of the stars. We can compute without much difficulty how often a star will pass our sun at a minimum distance less than that of Neptune. Such close approaches are rare. Our sun will, on the average, suffer only one in 10,000 cosmic years. The total effect probably would be very slight indeed. The chances are that the passing star would be fainter than our sun and, although the event would be front-page news for a while, no permanent harm of any sort would be done. The orbits of the planets around the sun would be changed, especially those of the outer planets, and Neptune or Pluto might join the interloper and leave the solar system. After the visit our sun with its flock of planets would move in a direction that would deviate by only 20° from its original path.

What are the chances that our sun might be hit by a passing neighbor? If that were to happen the results would be almost certainly catastrophic to life on the earth. But we probably have more immediate worries ahead of us, for the average interval between actual collisions of stars the size of our sun is of the order of 1,000,-000,000 (10^9) cosmic years or 100,000,000,000,000,000 (10^{17}) solar years! The only place where collisions might occur once in awhile is in the central core, but even here the chances are not good.

The rarity of the phenomenon is best illustrated if we note that in our galactic system, with its 200,000,000,000 stars, a collision between any two stars should occur only once in 1,000,000 years. If we consider that there are some regions of our galaxy where the stars are closer together than in our neighborhood and that some stars have much larger target areas than our sun, we might concede a somewhat higher probability for collisions. It is, however, very unlikely that, on the average, collisions take place more frequently than once in 10,000 years in any one galaxy.

From these simple computations it would seem that our chances of being put out of commission through a direct hit or close approach are very much less than the continued risk of being destroyed by comparatively small internal changes in the sun. As small a persistent change in the sun's total brightness as one magnitude would automatically result, in a fairly short interval of time, in a change of the average temperature of the earth by 75° centigrade. Such a change would not alter the planetary system as a whole, but it is improbable that life on the surface of the earth could adjust itself to an average temperature around the boiling point of water or to conditions prevailing at 50° centigrade below zero. A mild variability of our sun, something very much less drastic than a nova explosion, could easily put an end to all life on the earth.

But let us get back to our subject—stellar encounters. We have found already that spectacular close approaches are probably rather insignificant. The chances are that our sun will suffer only once in 1,000,000 cosmic years from an encounter that would swing it by a right angle from its original path. We should, however, not forget that the path of our sun is continually being changed to some extent by more distant passages. A single star passing at a distance of 1 light-year will change the direction of the sun's motion by somewhat less than 1 minute of arc. In the course of time the number of encounters within a few light-years of our sun is, however, quite large. Computations show that the total effect of all encounters at minimum distances less than 10 to 15 light-years between our sun and other stars will, in the course of one of our cosmic years, be about equal to the total effect produced by a single encounter of our sun and another star at a distance of 100 or 200 astronomical units. The greater importance of the unspectacular distant passages is demonstrated by the fact that a single encounter at a distance of 100 astronomical units should on the average happen only once in 2×10^{13} solar years or 100,000 cosmic years. It is quite clear that we might as well forget about the single right-angle encounters and the head on collisions and remember that the distant passages, because of their far greater frequency, are far more effective.

Our galaxy has not been rotating sufficiently long for the interchange of energy between stars of different types to become effective. From our considerations of stellar encounters it would seem

very unlikely that the stars would still show so much individuality in their motions if our galaxy had existed in its present form for as many as 10,000 cosmic years or 2×10^{12} solar years.

*　　*　　*

Our part of the galaxy is characterized by the presence of many loosely connected galactic clusters. Consider, for example, such clusters as the Hyades and the Pleiades. After our considerations of the disruptive effects of stellar encounters these clusters would hardly seem very stable objects. The Hyades are relatively so close to us that we have not only accurate measurements of the motions of the brighter members, but also a rather complete census of the total membership of the cluster. The densest part of the cluster lies at 130 light-years from the sun. It contains at most 150 members within a distance of 15 light-years from its center. The motions of the individual stars differ by not more than 0.5 kilometer per second from the average total motion.

We can predict what will probably happen to the Hyades cluster in the course of the next 10 or 20 cosmic years. The cluster ought to stay fairly close to the plane of our galaxy and move therefore in a region where the stars are probably spaced much as they are in the vicinity of the sun. We can easily compute how frequently a star which does not belong to the cluster, a field star, will pass through the cluster or how frequently one of them will pass by at a given distance.

Before we trace the effects of encounters on star clusters we should first look a little closer at the mechanics of a cluster free from intruders and passers-by. A cluster star that wanders slowly away from the rest of the group will generally be pulled back by the attraction of the whole mass. The cluster tries desperately to preserve its unity. But there is a villain in the piece! We know from observations on galactic rotation that the stars in the vicinity of the sun are all subject to the pull from the galactic nucleus. The parts of the cluster that are closest to the central nucleus of the galaxy will feel more of the nuclear pull than those that are farther away. The general galactic forces will therefore tend to shear the cluster apart. It becomes a regular tug of war. Can the force of attraction produced by the cluster as a whole pull hard enough to counter-

balance the disrupting "tidal" forces from the galactic nucleus? If the answer is yes, the cluster will hold together, but if not, then the cluster may soon be disrupted and its members strewn far and wide.

It takes some mathematical juggling to find where the dividing line will lie between clusters that can and those that cannot with-stand the shearing forces of galactic rotation. A certain average critical density is computed. A cluster for which the average star density is less than the critical value cannot possibly stay together, but one with an average density above the critical value will gen-erally have enough internal gravitational attraction to withstand the insidious disruptive forces from the galactic nucleus. A cluster for which the average density is equivalent to 10 solar masses for a cube 10 light-years on each side should stay together if, in the course of time, it does not come much closer to the galactic nucleus than does our sun.

What will be the probable effect of encounters between clusters and stars of the general field? The dimensions of the cluster will in general be large and the passing field star will therefore not affect all cluster members in the same way. Two cluster stars that were originally pursuing strictly parallel paths will probably move after the encounter in slightly diverging orbits. The net result of each encounter will be to loosen up the cluster. This will tend to weaken the cluster's attraction on its members and the general galactic tidal force may then get a chance to do its disruptive work.

The Hyades cluster is probably safe for at least 10 more of our cosmic years or for 2,000,000,000 solar years. By that time the en-counters with field stars will have done enough preliminary soften-ing up to bring the cluster to the brink of disruption. Sometime be-tween 10 and 15 cosmic years hence the galactic tidal force will become strongly effective. We may as well predict that 5,000,000,000 years from now you will look in vain for the remains of the Hyades cluster wherever you may search the galaxy.

We now turn to the more compact clusters, such as the Pleiades and Praesepe, whose average densities are about ten times that of the Hyades. These clusters are in a far better state than the Hyades to withstand the disruptive shearing forces of galactic rotation; the time scale for disruption from this cause alone is probably of the order of 100 cosmic years. But here a different process is at work and it moves sufficiently fast to eliminate from consideration dis-ruption by tidal forces: the Pleiades and Praesepe will probably suf-

fer a gradual internal collapse as a result of the escape of some of their members.

The process of collapse was first suggested in 1937 by Ambart-sumian and independently in 1940 by Spitzer. It operates as follows: in a fairly dense cluster encounters between two cluster members will be considerably more frequent than encounters between a cluster member and a field star. On occasion a cluster member involved in an encounter with one of its fellow members may acquire a velocity large enough to permit it to escape—to "evaporate"—from the cluster. The escaping star will carry with it more than its fair share of the available total energy of the cluster, leaving the remaining stars with a somewhat reduced average energy. When there is less energy per star, the star-members will not move quite so far from the center of the cluster as formerly. Hence the cluster will shrink. In the course of time many stars may escape, each of them taking with them more than their share of the total energy and, as the depletion progresses, a gradual collapse of the cluster will ensue.

The rate of escape will be slowed down somewhat, as Chandrasekhar has shown, because a *dynamical friction* is exerted by the slower-moving stars upon the escaping stars, but the total effect, after correction for dynamical friction, still leads to the gradual dismemberment and slow collapse of clusters like the Pleiades and Praesepe. The predicted times in which collapse should take place are of the order of a few billion solar years—20 cosmic years, more or less.

From a purely dynamical point of view, the time scale for important dynamical changes in the galactic clusters of our galaxy seems to be of the order of 20 cosmic years. At the moment the Hyades, the Pleiades, and Praesepe are among the more conspicuous features of our galaxy. If we were to return in 10 or 20 cosmic years, these clusters would either have evaporated or collapsed—and there seem to be no others slated to take their place. One might be tempted to think about dismembered globular clusters as possible future Pleiades-like clusters, but two considerations show how impossible this would be. In the first place, globular clusters with their characteristic spectrum-luminosity diagram cannot change into clusters with Pleiades-like arrays. Second, calculations readily show that the rate of evaporation for globular clusters is far too slow to lead to anything of the size and with the membership of the Pleiades cluster in 20 or even in 100 cosmic years. Dynamically, the globular clusters are among the most stable features of our galaxy.

There seems to be no escape from the hypothesis that the composition of our galaxy changes markedly in 20 or so cosmic years. It is significant that this interval agrees closely with the estimated age of our earth, which is 5 billion solar years or 25 cosmic years, and hence it is tempting to consider 20 or 30 cosmic years as a probable minimum age for our galaxy.

Might it be possible that other Hyades- or Pleiades-like clusters are now being formed from field stars? We do not pretend to know from where the clusters came, but from a purely mechanical point of view it seems very unlikely that a workable mechanism could be found for the building up of clusters by chance encounters of unattached stars. Another suggestion is that new galactic clusters are being formed steadily by the process of the breaking up of clouds of interstellar gas and dust, followed by the collapse of the separate small clouds, or globules, into the stars that are the members of the newborn clusters. Such processes are rather likely to occur and it is not impossible—as has been suggested by McCrea and others—that there may be a continuing process of formation and evolutionary decline of galactic clusters and associations of O and B stars, with the number of clusters and associations presumably not varying much in the course of time. For the galactic clusters with stars of spectral types A and later, the rate of depletion seems faster than the rate of formation of new clusters and these are probably a vanishing species.

We have, of course, no information about the numbers of galactic clusters that there were in the sky at the time when the first cockroaches began to march over the face of the earth, a time which, according to the paleontologists, is about 1.5 cosmic years ago. We know even less about the make-up of our galaxy at the time of the birth of our earth—an event that happened presumably some 20 or 30 cosmic years ago. The rate of disappearance of the galactic clusters that we know today is so high that it would seem extremely unlikely that our galaxy could have existed in its present form for much longer than 50 of our cosmic years.

* *

*

The Expanding Universe and The Cosmic Time Scale

In the present volume, we are primarily concerned with our home galaxy, the Milky Way system. Another time interval, however,

that must be closely related to the time scale of cosmic development is the time since the beginning of expansion in the universe of galaxies. Forty years ago, astronomers at the Lowell and Mount Wilson Observatories noticed that the spectra of some of the fainter external galaxies were very peculiar. The spectra resemble closely that of the sun, but the surprising thing is that the absorption lines are in most cases shifted toward the red end of the spectrum. The fainter galaxies generally exhibit the greater shifts. Displacements have been observed for some of the more distant galaxies that are so large that the K line of ionized calcium, which is normally at 3933 angstroms, is found near the normal position of the hydrogen line at 4341 angstroms.

A detailed discussion of this red shift is out of place in a book on the Milky Way, but it is clear that the motion away from our galaxy of all the external galaxies can be explained as a consequence of expansion of the entire system. Working back from the observed relation between the velocity of recession and the present distances of the galaxies, we can estimate how long the universe of galaxies may have been expanding. These computations show that, if the red shift is explained as a velocity shift, the expansion of the universe of galaxies would probably have begun some 4 to 5 billion years ago. The close agreement of this value of the cosmic time scale with our previous estimates is indeed encouraging, especially since the new evidence is of an entirely different character from what we had so far presented. The case for a true expansion of the universe of galaxies has been strengthened greatly by two recent discoveries in the field of radio astronomy. The first is the discovery by Lilley and McClain of a neutral hydrogen absorption feature in the 21-centimeter profile for the Cygnus radio source; it is shifted in frequency by precisely the amount required if the hydrogen cloud that produces it is receding with the optically known radial velocity of the Cygnus source. The second discovery is one by Heeschen of 21-centimeter emission from the Coma cluster of galaxies, again shifted in frequency by the amount expected on the basis of the optically determined radial velocity of recession of the Coma cluster.

Before we begin to feel too vain about the way in which the pieces of our cosmic jigsaw puzzle are fitting together, we should point to some of the weak points in the argument. What is it that we really observe for the faint galaxies? The basic observation is that the spectrum lines are shifted progressively further toward longer wavelengths as we observe more distant systems. Such observations can be explained most naturally by postulating an expansion of the whole universe of galaxies. But other explanations are within the realm of possibility. Until precise colors and magnitudes, as well as classifications, become available for many faint galaxies with known red shifts, it will not be possible to rule out definitely interpretations in terms of phenomena that produce red shifts but that do not involve true velocities of expansion. In a nonexpanding universe, the derived interval of 4 to 5 billion years may be meaningless and have no relevance for the time scale of cosmic development. For the present, however, most astrophysicists and cosmologists are inclined to consider the red shift as resulting from a true expansion, and the agreement between the time scales for the development of the earth, for the galactic clusters, and for the universe of galaxies appears to be significant. Four to 5 billion years does seem to be the best estimate for the time interval that has elapsed since our universe passed through a catastrophic upheaval, possibly—though here we are on very uncertain grounds—one that marked the very birth of our universe.

*   *

*

Star Birth and Evolution   Our estimates for the cosmic time scale have been based on data from stellar motions and the arrangement of stars in systems. What about the stars themselves? They ought to have some voice in the matter, for they are asked to supply energy for millions and millions of years. It is all well and good to talk in terms of 5 billion years, but can the stars keep shining for so long a time?

Other volumes in the series of Harvard Books on Astronomy consider carefully the processes by which our sun and other stars are continually supplied with energy for radiation. The familiar processes of chemical burning have no place in the scheme. It is so hot in stellar interiors that the atoms are stripped of most of their outer electrons. Transformations as superficial as those of molecular chemistry can take place in the atmospheres of some cool stars and in our laboratories on the earth, but not in stellar interiors. At the high temperatures prevailing inside the stars, physics looks for the source of stellar energy in the changes that must take place in the atomic nuclei. The interior temperature rises steadily from 6000°C at the surface of the sun to some 20,000,000°C in the central region.

At these tremendously high central temperatures the atomic nuclei, freed from most of their customary neutralizing entourage of electrons, move at such speeds that violent changes occur when two such nuclei collide. Hydrogen nuclei—the familiar protons— collide with other hydrogen nuclei and with the nuclei of heavier atoms. These collisions lead to the formation of heavier nuclei, notably of helium; in some stars this comes about through a transformation cycle in which the carbon nucleus figures prominently as a catalytic agent, in others through direct interaction of protons with other protons. We need not consider here just how these nuclear transformations operate, but the important fact is that two protons and two neutrons with a total mass of 4.033 atomic mass units must combine to form a helium nucleus, whose mass is 4.004 on the same scale. A small fraction of the original mass—about 0.7 percent—is therefore lost in the course of the nuclear construction. This mass is transformed into radiative energy according to the famous Einstein equation,

$$E = mc^2,$$

which relates the mass loss m to the corresponding released energy E, where c represents the velocity of light. The transformation of hydrogen into helium is the most effective process of energy generation at work in stellar interiors. Stars that have exhausted their plentiful original supply of hydrogen have some secondary nuclear processes on which to call, but none are so effective in releasing free radiative energy. Annihilation of matter at very high temperatures would presumably be a still more effective process, but we do not seem to find anywhere in the universe temperatures high enough for this process to occur.

Let us now see how well the stars can get along in their evolution if they depend entirely on the energy produced by the transformation of hydrogen into helium. Our sun, an average dwarf G star, radiates at a rather low rate; it should use up about 1 percent of its mass in hydrogen in 1,000,000,000 years, that is in about 5 cosmic years. With about 60 percent of the sun's mass still hydrogen, the sun has enough nuclear fuel left to shine as it does now for another 100 cosmic years or longer. But the picture is not so cheerful when we turn to typical A stars, like Sirius, with an absolute magnitude

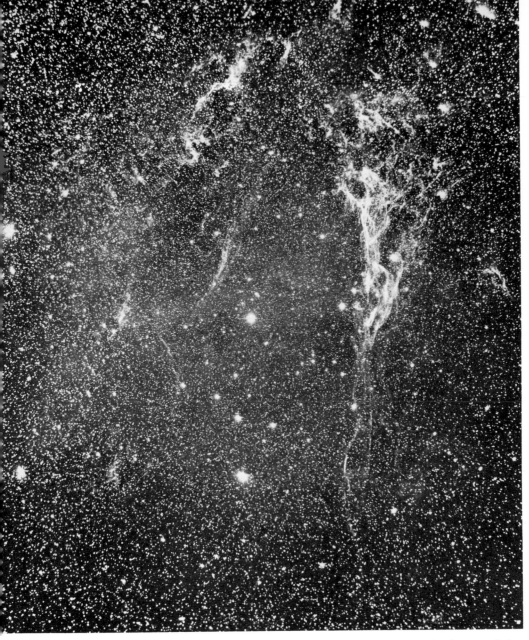

Fig. 124. The central part of the Network in Cygnus, showing the intricate emission nebulosity. See Fig. 125. (Lick Observatory photograph, Crossley reflector.)

three to four magnitudes brighter than our sun, which entails sending out between 15 and 40 times as much energy per unit time. The masses of such stars are no more than two or three solar masses, so that the energy that must be generated per unit mass is 10 to 15 times as great as for the sun. Such a star should use up 1 percent of its mass as hydrogen nuclear fuel within half a cosmic year or so

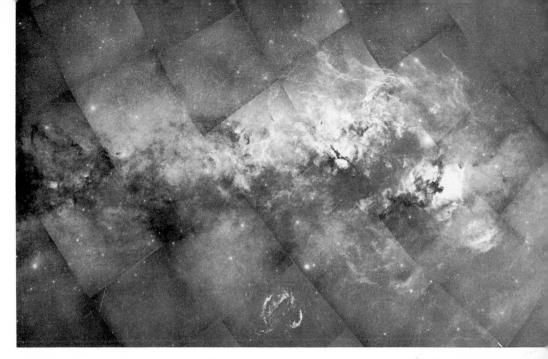

Fig. 125. A section of the northern Milky Way. The mosaic photograph shows the Milky Way. from Cygnus to Aquila. On the right is the North America Nebula (see also Figs. 66, 67, and 87), and the Cygnus Cloud is to the right and above the center of the picture. Below the center are the Veil and the Network Nebulae; for a detailed photograph of a portion of the Network Nebula, see Fig. 124. The photograph is a reverse print as can be readily seen from an inspection of the N. America Nebula. The Great Rift of the Milky Way runs horizontally through the center of the picture. (National Geographic Society-Palomar Observatory Sky Survey.)

and it can hardly have sent out energy at its present rate for as long as 20 cosmic years. The A stars can hence barely have existed since the time of the birth of our earth, and they must be getting near the end of their available supply of nuclear hydrogen fuel.

What about the O and B stars, which may shine with intrinsic brightnesses equivalent to 10,000 suns and which have masses less than 100 times that of our sun? Here the nuclear processes must be producing energy at rates at least 100 times as fast as in the sun and the total supply of nuclear fuel should be exhausted in 1 cosmic year or less. The O and B stars may therefore be of very recent origin and we are forced to look—a not unpleasant task!—for places in our Milky Way system where the process of star birth may be observed today. Hoyle, Bondi, McCrea, and others have suggested that the massive stars may replenish their exhausted energy sources by *accretion*, that is, by the capture of matter from interstellar space. This process is probably not a very effective one. In order to acquire any appreciable quantity of matter by accretion, a star must be practically at rest relative to the interstellar medium, and the radiation pressure it exerts on the particles of the medium must not be sufficiently great to counterbalance the tendency of matter to fall into the star's atmosphere. Neither condition appears to be satisfied by the spendthrift O and B stars.

We turn back to the O–B associations and aggregates that were described in Chapter 4. We found several of them to be expanding and, when we retraced their development in time, we found that the expansion in at least four well-established cases must have begun only 0.1 cosmic year ago. The short maximum lifetimes for O and B stars and the expansion phenomena in O–B associations agree if one supposes that the associations and their component stars are—cosmically—of very recent origin. Some were apparently formed a small fraction of a cosmic year ago—a very short time compared to the age of our earth of 20 to 25 cosmic years!

It is noteworthy that the O and B stars—which are known to be first-rate spiral tracers (see Chapter 9)—occur especially in parts of the Milky Way where interstellar gas and dust are plentiful. It is tempting to hunt for relatively small condensations of interstellar gas and dust and look upon them as possible protostars. The small *globules* that are often seen projected against the luminous peripheral edges of emission nebulae, appear to come closest to the protostars for which we are searching. They are found especially in the turbulent regions of high gas pressure near the outer boundaries of regions of ionized hydrogen—the H(II) regions. Presumably contraction will take place, possibly at first through pressure effects, then through the self-gravitation of the globules, which may grow in the meantime slowly through the accretion of gas and dust. This contraction should continue until the particles inside the globule shatter in collisions to become molecules and then atoms. Finally the atomic nuclei move sufficiently fast that nuclear transformations result from collisions. When nuclear transformations occur, the collapse should slow down and gradually come to a halt . . . a star would have been born.

All of the above considerations are of course highly speculative and many details will have to be elaborated before the present picture can be considered more than a good working hypothesis. But it is encouraging to find that the presence of expanding associations of spendthrift stars may be understood as part of a coherent scheme of star formation and evolution.

The present volume is obviously not the place to enter into a

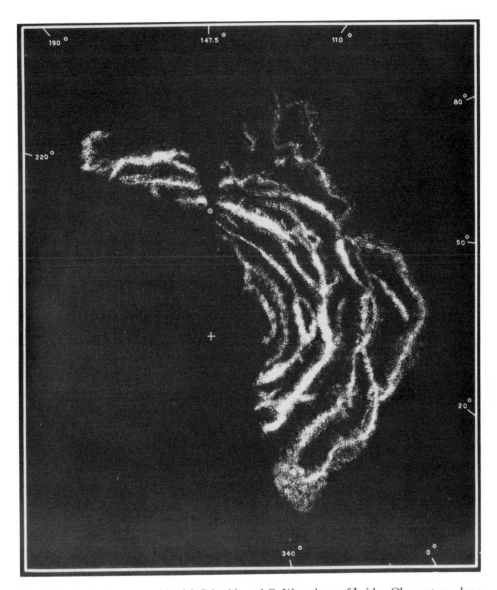

Fig. 126.   A sketch prepared by M. Schmidt and G. Westerhout of Leiden Observatory, showing their impression of the spiral structure of our Milky Way system as revealed by the Leiden
observations of 21-cm radiation from neutral hydrogen. The cross marks the position of the
center of our galaxy and the sun's position is shown. Galactic longitudes are marked along the
edge. The pie-shaped black gap above the sun point covers the region in which all galactic rotation effects are absent and for which the distribution of hydrogen in depth cannot be determined. The results from the Southern Hemisphere are not included in this diagram.

lengthy discussion of theories of the nature of the universe of galaxies. We should, however, mention that Hoyle and Bondi and their associates have made the suggestion of the *continuous creation of matter*. As the universe expands, it would decrease steadily in average density. Hoyle and Bondi suppose that new matter is being created—from nowhere and by an undefined physical process—at a rate that is precisely the right one to keep the average density constant. One of the by-products of the theory of continuous creation is that it would provide for an ever-present supply of hydrogen fuel for our nuclear processes. The Hoyle and Bondi theory has relatively few supporters, but it deserves to be recognized as a completely new approach to the problems of stellar birth and evolution. Dissatisfaction with the generally accepted theories of constantly operating thermonuclear reactions in stellar interiors has also been expressed by Ambartsumian, who recommends that astrophysicists pay more careful attention to the possibilities of sudden explosive releases of energy, as seem indicated by the observations of T Tauri stars and short-lived flares in intrinsically very faint stars.

*   *

*

Looking Ahead

The reader may have felt some dissatisfaction with this chapter because we have had to make so many assumptions. Yet we believe that we can defend our interest in time scales and evolution against the assaults of critics. In the universe as we observe it, we find certain rules and regularities. We naturally ask what are the consequences of these observed conditions and what changes will take place as time progresses. It is then only a step to speculations about the far and distant past, the cosmic time scale, and stellar evolution.

The methodical study of the past of our universe has great value in directing our attention to special problems that require observational study. The search for stars that are unusually bright or unusually faint is made more interesting by our realization that the discovery of one or two such stars may have important bearings on our ideas about stellar birth and evolution and the cosmic time scale. It is essential for science that we realize the limitations of each special field of research, but it is also essential that we do not retreat too soon from the unknown. Cosmological speculations have been a wonderful stimulant, not only to Milky Way research, but also to the whole of modern astronomy and astrophysics.

Index